Singing and Rhyming

BY

LILLA BELLE PITTS

PROFESSOR OF MUSIC EDUCATION, Teachers College, Columbia University, New York

MABELLE GLENN

FORMERLY DIRECTOR OF MUSIC, Public Schools, Kansas City, Missouri

LORRAIN E. WATTERS

DIRECTOR OF MUSIC, Public Schools, Des Moines, Iowa

ILLUSTRATIONS BY Alison Cummings and Eloise Wilkin

GINN AND COMPANY

BOSTON · NEW YORK · CHICAGO · ATLANTA · DALLAS · COLUMBUS · SAN FRANCISCO · TORONTO · LONDON

Acknowledgments

Acknowledgment is due to publishers, composers, and authors for permission to reprint songs and poems in this book, as follows.

MARJORIE BARROWS, "Pine Tree Song"; Estate of KATHARINE LEE BATES, "America the Beautiful"; B. T. BATSFORD LTD., "The Little Grey Squirrel," by VERNON HART, from HENRY CALDWELL COOK's Homework and Hobbyhorses; THE BOBBS-MERRILL COMPANY, Inc., lines from "A Boy's Mother," from Rhymes of Childhood, by JAMES WHITCOMB RILEY; MRS. A. McK. GIFFORD, "Evening Song" (Little Child, Good Child), from Crack o' Dawn, by FANNIE STEARNS DAVIS; FRANCES DENSMORE, "On the Ground Here I Lie"; KENTON KILMER, "Easter," from Poems, Essays and Letters, by JOYCE KILMER, copyright 1914, 1917, 1918, by DOUBLEDAY & COMPANY, INC.; EDUCATIONAL PUBLISHING CORPORATION, "January," by ALICE E. ALLEN, from Choral Speaking, published by the EDUCATIONAL PUBLISHING CORPORATION, Darien, Connecticut; H. T. FITZSIMONS COMPANY, "Old Roger Is Dead," from Old English and American Games; "Who's In?" by ELIZABETH FLEMING, courtesy of the author; FOLLETT PUBLISHING COMPANY, "The Aeroplane," from Around a Toadstool Table, by ROWENA BASTIN BENNETT; FRANCES FROST, "Woodchuck Hill"; GINN AND COMPANY and the editors of THE WORLD OF MUSIC, "Brothers, Let Us Dance," from Listen and Sing, copyright 1936, 1943, "Jingle at the Window" and "Skip to My Lou," from Tuning Up, copyright 1936, 1943, and "Klein, Klein Kleuterken," from On Wings of Song, copyright 1945; GINN AND COMPANY, "Marching Song" (words), by LAURA E. RICHARDS, from The Magic of Song, and "The Night Wind's Lullaby," from Adventures in Music, both of THE MUSIC EDUCATION SERIES, and "The Lamplighter," from The Latin-American Song Book, copyright 1942 by GINN AND COMPANY; MRS. GEORGINA GUERRA, "Snow-White Little Burro"; HARPER & BROTHERS, "Trucks," from I Go a-Traveling, by JAMES S. TIPPETT, copyright 1929 by HARPER & BROTHERS, and " 'Spress" (I Love to Hear the Train), from Bread 'n Jam, by WYMOND GARTHWAITE, copyright 1928 by HARPER & BROTHERS; WILLIAM HEINEMANN, LTD., "White Butterflies," by ALGERNON CHARLES SWINBURNE; HENRY HOLT AND COMPANY and V. F. BARTON, "The Cupboard," from Collected Poems by WALTER DE LA MARE, copyright 1920 by HENRY HOLT AND COMPANY, "Rain," from A Pocketful of Posies, by ABBIE FARWELL BROWN; LOIS LENSKI, "People," from Skipping Village, by LOIS LENSKI; LITTLE, BROWN & COMPANY, "At Easter Time" and "A Sleigh-Ride," from In My Nursery, by LAURA E. RICHARDS; LONGMANS, GREEN AND COMPANY, "Who Will Come with Me" (Jolly Rover), from Singing Circle, by LADY BELL; THE MACMILLAN COMPANY, "Rain in the City," from The Pointed People, by RACHEL FIELD, copyright 1924 and 1930 by THE MACMILLAN COMPANY and used with their permission; "High, Betty Martin," from Folk Songs of Old New England, by ELOISE HUBBARD LINSCOTT, copyright 1939 by THE MACMILLAN COMPANY and used with their permission; "White Fields," from The Rocky Road to Dublin, by JAMES STEPHENS, copyright 1915 by THE MACMILLAN COMPANY and used with their permission; lines from "Lincoln, the Man of the People," by EDWIN MARKHAM, reprinted by permission; SEÑORA MARÍA CADILLA DE MARTÍNEZ, "Six Little Dogs" and "White Dove," from Cantos y Juegos Infantiles de Puerto Rico; NOBLE AND NOBLE, PUBLISHERS, INC., "We Thank Thee" (second stanza), by MATTIE M. RENWICK, from DEMING's Pieces for Every Day the Schools Celebrate; NORTHERN MUSIC CORPORATION, "Lock and Key," by FRANK LUTHER; JUNE M. NORTON and MARGARET I. SIMPSON, "Gobble! Gobble! Gobble!" from the June Norton Sing-It-Again Book; OXFORD UNIVERSITY PRESS, "Donkey Riding," reprinted from the Oxford Song Book, by permission of OXFORD UNIVERSITY PRESS, "Hail on the Pine Tree" and "The Moon Ship," reprinted from A Year of Japanese Epigrams by WILLIAM N. PORTER, by permission of the OXFORD UNIVERSITY PRESS; G. P. PUTNAM's SONS, lines from "Play" in Verses and Fly Leaves, by CHARLES STUART CALVERLEY, and lines from the Dedication in Everything and Anything, by DOROTHY ALDIS, copyright 1925, 1926, 1927 by DOROTHY ALDIS, courtesy of G. P. PUTNAM's SONS; SIR ISAAC PITMAN & SONS, Limited, "A Farmer Went to Market," from Songs and Marching Tunes for Children, by PAUL EDMONDS; CHARLES SCRIBNER's SONS, "We-um," from Grammar School Songs, by CHARLES FARNSWORTH; THE SOCIETY OF AUTHORS, "I Wake in the Morning Early," from The Fairy Flute, "Mary Middling," from Fifty-One New Nursery Rhymes, and "Tadpoles," from Here We Come a-Piping, all by ROSE FYLEMAN, by permission of THE SOCIETY OF AUTHORS, MISS ROSE FYLEMAN, and MESSRS. METHUEN; NANCY BYRD TURNER, "Song at Dusk" and lines from "Washington"; LOUIS UNTERMEYER, lines from "The Land of Halloween," by NANCY BIRCKHEAD, and from "Spring Ring Jingle," by MICHAEL LEWIS, both from Rainbow in the Sky, published by HARCOURT, BRACE AND COMPANY; ROBERTA M. WHITEHEAD, "If You Look and Listen"; WHITMAN PUBLISHING COMPANY, "Balloon Man" and "Sleigh Ride," from 365 Bedtime Nursery Rhymes; YALE UNIVERSITY PRESS, "September," from Sea Moods and Other Poems, by EDWARD BLISS REED; ISLA P. RICHARDSON, for her poem "Snowflakes."

In the case of some poems for which acknowledgment is not given, we have earnestly endeavored to find the original source and to procure permission for their use, but without success.

Contents

❧

SONGS WE KNOW · (Page 7)

ABOUT FOLKS · (Page 15)

PLAYTIME SONGS

JUST FOR FUN

WORKADAY SONGS

SINGING GAMES

PEOPLE WE LIKE TO KNOW

SONGLAND PEOPLE

HOME AND FAMILY

GETTING UP AND GOING TO BED

SONGS OF DEVOTION

About Happy Holidays

BIRTHDAY

COLUMBUS DAY

HALLOWEEN

THANKSGIVING

The covers now are opened wide
So turn the page and step inside
And you will find some children who
Are doing things you always do.
                    Dorothy Aldis

I pledge allegiance to the flag
of the United States of America
and to the Republic for which it stands,
one nation, indivisible,
with liberty and justice for all.

SONGS
WE KNOW

Out on the breeze,
O'er land and seas,
A beautiful banner is streaming;
Shining its stars,
Splendid its bars,
Under the sunshine 'tis gleaming.
Hail to the flag,
The dear, bonny flag—
The flag that is red, white, and blue.

Lydia Avery Coonley Ward

There Are Many Flags in Many Lands

M. H. Howliston

Composer Unknown

There are man-y flags in man-y lands, There are flags of ev-'ry hue;

But there is no flag, how-ev-er grand, Like our own Red, White and Blue.

CHORUS

Then hur-rah for the flag, Our coun-try's flag, Its stripes and white stars, too;

There is no flag in an-y land, Like our own Red, White and Blue.

7

Chicchirichi[1]

Translated   Italian Children's Song

mi

"Chic-chi-ri-chi, we're three lit-tle ants."

"Cuc-cu-ru-cu,[2] where are you go-ing?"

"Chic-chi-ri-chi, to take a bath."

"Cuc-cu-ru-cu, when will you come back?"

"Chic-chi-ri-chi, we'll come this eve-ning."

"Cuc-cu-ru-cu, we'll ask you to sup-per."

[1]Pronounce kee-kee-ree-kee [2]Pronounce coo-coo-roo-coo

"Chic-chi - ri - chi, what will there be?"

"Cuc-cu - ru - cu, some meat and spa-ghet - ti."

Swing High, Swing Low

Alice B. Haines

Louella Garrett

Swing · high, swing low, swing · high, swing low,

First up in the tree tops a - sail - ing we go!

Then down to the ground where the soft grass - es grow.

Swing · high, swing low, swing · high, swing low!

9

The Bus

Play Song

so

1. The peo-ple on the bus go up and down,
2. The wheels · on the bus go round and round,
3. The horn · on the bus goes too, too, too.
4. The mon-ey in the box goes ding, ding, ding,

Up and down, up and down.
Round and round, round and round.
Too, too, too, too, too, too.
Ding, ding, ding, ding, ding, ding.

The peo-ple on the bus go up and down,
The wheels · on the bus go round and round,
The horn · on the bus goes too, too, too,
The mon-ey in the box goes ding, ding, ding.

1, 2, 3, 4. All through the town.

5. The wiper on the glass goes swish, swish, swish,
Swish, swish, swish, swish, swish, swish.
The wiper on the glass goes swish, swish, swish,
All through the town.

6. The driver on the bus says, "Move on back,
Move on back, move on back."
The driver on the bus says, "Move on back,"
All through the town.

10

Bluebird, Bluebird

Folk Game (Texas style)

Blue-bird, blue-bird through my win-dow, Blue-bird, blue-bird through my win-dow,

Stand in circle, hands joined and held high to form windows. Child who is bluebird flies in and out windows.

Blue-bird, blue-bird through my win-dow, Oh, John-ny, aren't you tired?

Take a lit-tle girl and tap her on the shoul-der,
boy   him

Bluebird taps partner on shoulder.   These two fly in and out the windows.

Take a lit-tle girl and tap her on the shoul-der,
boy   him

Take a lit-tle girl and tap her on the shoul-der,
boy   him

Oh, John-ny, aren't you tired?

The second time the song is sung the two bluebirds choose new partners, the third time four bluebirds, and so on.

11

Hush, My Baby

Mississippi Lullaby

Hush, my ba - by, don't you cry, Dad-dy's going to come home by and by.

He will bring to his dear lit - tle ba - by

Can-dy and a kit - ty and a pup-py-dog may-be.

slower and very softly

Hush, hush, hush and don't you cry, Dad-dy's going to come home by and by.

Yankee Doodle

Traditional

1. Fath'r and I went down to camp, A - long with Cap-tain Good - win,
2. There was Cap-tain Wash-ing-ton, Up - on a slap-ping stal - lion,

And there we saw the men and boys, As thick as hast-y pud-ding.
A - giv-ing or-ders to his men; I guess there was a mil - lion.

CHORUS

Yan-kee Doo-dle keep it up,   Yan-kee Doo-dle dan - dy,

Mind the mu-sic   and the step, And with the girls be hand - y.

Jingle at the Window

Traditional Singing Game

mi

Pass one win-dow, ti - de - o,   Pass two win-dows, ti - de - o,

Single circle of partners, each child's left hand on right shoulder of the child ahead. Group moves in circle.

Pass three win-dows, ti - de - o,   Jin-gle at the win-dows, ti - de - o.

Ti - de - o,   ti - de - o,   Jin-gle at the win-dows, ti - de - o,

Boy locks right elbow with girl behind him and swings.

Ti - de - o,   ti - de - o,   Jin-gle at the win-dows, ti - de - o.

Lock left elbows and swing.

Shake the Apple Tree

Like a folk song

Carl Reinecke

Hap-py lit-tle John-nie, Pol-ly, come with me;

Come in-to the gar-den, Shake the ap-ple tree;

I will shake the big ones, You will shake the small;

When we've filled our bas-ket Home we'll take them all.

Hap-py lit-tle John-nie, Shake the ap-ple tree.

14

ABOUT FOLKS

Tall people, short people,
Thin people, fat;
Lady so dainty,
Wearing a hat.
Straight people, dumpy people,
Man dressed in brown;
Baby in a buggy,
These make a Town.

Lois Lenski

Playtime Songs

Fol-de-rol and riddle-ma-ree,
Come and join my jubilee.

Michael Lewis

Rig-a-Jig-Jig

Singing Game

As I was walk-ing down the street, Heigh-o, heigh-o, heigh-o, heigh-o,

A pret-ty girl I chanced to meet, Heigh-o, heigh-o, heigh-o.
(nice young man)

Rig-a-jig-jig, and a-way we go, A-way we go, a-way we go;

Rig-a-jig-jig, and a-way we go, Heigh-o, heigh-o, · heigh-o.

Sing Together

Round

Sing, sing to-geth-er, mer-ri-ly, mer-ri-ly sing;

16

mi mi mi mi so

Sing, sing to - geth - er, mer - ri - ly, mer - ri - ly sing;

so do

Sing, sing, sing, sing.

Come, Let Us Dance

L. B. P.

do ti la so fa mi mi re do

"Come, let us dance!" the pret - ty girls cried.

"We'll whis-tle you a tune!" the boys re - plied.

"So mi so so so fa la la, re fa fa fa mi so so."

(Or whistle)

Skip-ping, trip-ping to and fro the mer-ry girls will go.

17

Come, Let's Be Merry

L. B. P.   English Country Dance

do   do   ti   la   la   so   so fa mi

Come, let's be mer-ry,   come, let's be gay

And we'll sing and play the   live-long day.

Sing-ing and danc-ing,   it   is such fun;

mi   re do

So we'll play un-til   the   day   is done.

Listen to "Country Gardens," Grainger. (Victor Rhythm Album Six.)

One For the Money

do

One for the mon-ey, Two for the show, Three to make read-y, And four to go.

Catch Me If You Can

Sally Bowen

do re mi fa so la ti do la so

Up the hill went Ned, Call-ing as he ran,

"Catch me! Catch me! Catch me if you can!"

Down the hill went Sue, Call-ing as she ran,

"Catch me! Catch me! Catch me if you can!"

Diving

Flora I. Johanson

Francis Hilliard

do do do so la ti do

Heave ho! A - way we go Down to the pool to dive,

The wa-ter is cold, but a sail-or bold Al-ways comes up a - live.

19

Marching and Running

When we're march - ing on our street

Left, right, left, right go our feet.

When we're run - ning, run - ning on our street

Run, run, run, run, run, run, run, run go our feet.

Running and Walking

Teacher sings

Run - ning, run - ning, run - ning, run - ning, run - ning with me.

You make up your "answer."

Walk, walk, walk, walk, walk with me.

Listen to "Silhouette," Rheinhold. (Victor Rhythm Album Three.) When you listen to this music see where you feel like walking and where you feel like running.

Skipping and Galloping

do

Let's go skip - ping on our street,

Skip - ty, skip - ty, skip - ty, skip - ty go our feet.

Now we're po - nies on our street,

Gal-lop-ing, gal-lop-ing, gal-lop-ing, gal-lop-ing go our feet.

Walking and Skipping

Teacher sings.

do

Walk, walk, walk, walk, walk with me.

You make up your "answer."

Skip-ty, skip-ty, skip-ty, skip-ty, skip-ty, skip with me.

Listen to "Theme for Skipping," Anderson. (Victor Rhythm Album One.)

Intry Mintry

Counting-out Song

mi

In-try min-try cu-try corn, Ap-ple seed and ap-ple thorn.

Wi-re bri-ar, lim-ber-lock, Five wild geese all in a flock.

Turn and turn and turn a-bout, O - U - T and it spells "OUT."

Roller Skating

Christine Turner Curtis

June Goethe Garrels

mi re do mi re do re la la

1. Skate a - long, straight a - long down the street,
2. Coast a - long, coast a - long down the hill,

Fly - ing feet car - ry you mer - ri - ly;
Take a spill, pick your - self up and then

Listen to "Skating," Kullak. (Victor Rhythm Album Two.)

Roll a-long, bowl a-long, o-ver and down;
Race a-long, chase a-long, cir-cle and fly

Clack-e-ty, in-to the town.
Swift as a bird in the sky.

Swing Song

Christine Turner Curtis   Harvey Worthington Loomis

do ti la so la mi so re so mi so

1. Un-der the leaf-y elm tree, swing-ing, swing-ing,
2. O-ver the world of blos-som, swing-ing, swing-ing,

do ti la so la ti re la re so

Un-der the sun and shad-ow, to and fro.
O-ver the lawns and gar-dens, high and low;

Sum-mer-y winds are bring-ing tin-kle of cow-bells ring-ing,
Up where the birds are wing-ing, up where the leaves are sing-ing,

While we go swing-ing, swing-ing, high and low.
On we go swing-ing, sing-ing as we go.

Listen to "Valse Gracieuse," Dvořák. (Victor Rhythm Album Three.)

23

I Had a Little Monkey

Ball-bouncing Song

so   do   re   mi   fa   so   so

1. I had a lit-tle mon-key, His name was Slim-zy Jim. ·
2. I have a lit-tle broth-er, His name is Ti-ny Tim. ·

I put him in a row-boat And sent him out to swim, ·
I put him in a bath-tub To teach him how to swim, ·

He fell in-to the wa-ter, He broke his wool-ly head
He drank up all the wa-ter! He ate up all the soap!

And now my lit-tle mon-key Is dead, · dead, · dead, ·
Now ev-'ry time he talks There's a bub-ble in his throat,

And now my lit-tle mon-key Is dead, · dead, · dead. ·
Now ev-'ry time he talks There's a bub-ble in his throat. ·

Bounce balls or skip ropes to "Theme for Skipping," Anderson. (Victor Rhythm Album One.)

24

I Went Upstairs

Rope-jumping Song

mi do do mi mi do do mi

I went up-stairs to make my bed,

I made a mis-take, and I bumped my head.

mi re do do la so

Just a-jump-ing this rope, just a-jump-ing this rope,

Just a-jump-ing this rope to - day.

To - mor-row, to - mor-row, to - mor-row nev - er comes,

To - mor-row, to - mor-row, to - mor-row al - ways runs.

Singing Along

L. B. P.

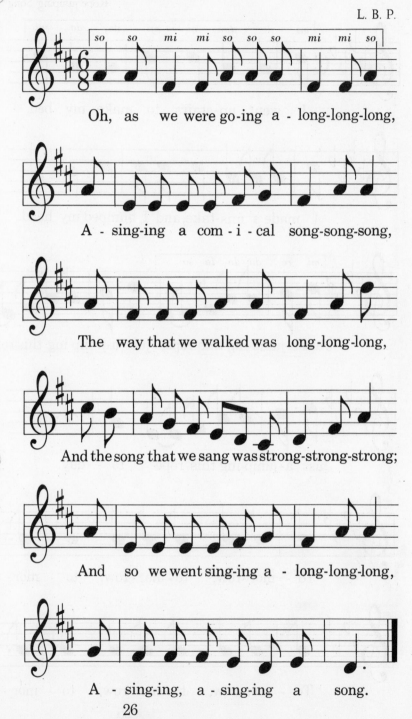

so   so   mi   mi   so   so   so   mi   mi   so

Oh, as   we were go-ing a - long-long-long,

A - sing-ing   a com - i - cal   song-song-song,

The   way that we walked was   long-long-long,

And the song that we sang was strong-strong-strong;

And   so we went sing-ing a - long-long-long,

A - sing-ing, a - sing-ing   a   song.

26

Lock and Key

Frank Luther

You are a gold lock, *(You are a gold lock.)* I am a gold key; *(I am a gold key.)*

You are a sil-ver lock, *(You are a sil-ver lock.)* I am a sil-ver key; *(I am a sil-ver key.)*

You are a brass lock, *(You are a brass lock.)* I am a brass key; *(I am a brass key.)*

You are a lead lock, *(You are a lead lock.)* I am a lead key; *(I am a lead key.)*

You are a tin lock, *(You are a tin lock.)* I am a tin key; *(I am a tin key.)*

You are a monk lock, *(You are a monk lock.)* I am a mon-key! *(I am a mon-key!)*

Listen to this song sung by Frank Luther. (Children's Corner, Decca Album) Some of you may wish to sing the "echo" while the piano is playing the tune an octave higher.

29

Joe and Jess

Louella Garrett

so mi la so mi do re mi re mi do

1. Joe on - ly knew one word and that was no.
2. Jess on - ly knew one word and that was yes.

He was told to learn some more, but Joe said, "No!" .
He was told one word won't do, but Jess said, "Yes!" .

He met a can - dy man one day
He met a pop - corn man one day

Who said, "I am giv - ing my can - dy a - way."
Who said, "This is free, will you throw it a - way?"

Joe on - ly knew one word. Joe said, "No!" .
Jess on - ly knew one word. Jess said, "Yes!" .

30

Nineteen Birds

M. L. Elliott

J. W. Elliott

so   do   so   so   so   re   so

1. Nine-teen birds   and   one   bird more,
2. To   the   score   then   add   but   one;
3. Now   add   two,   and   you   will   see

They make twen - ty, and that's   a   score.
That will make on - ly   twen - ty - one.
Then you'll add   up to   twen - ty - three.

4. If you like these clever tricks,
   Add three more to make twenty-six.

5. Then three more, if you have time;
   Now you've got up to twenty-nine.

6. Twenty-nine now quickly take,
   Add one more and you thirty make.

One, Two, Three, Four

Children's Rhyme

1. One,   two,   three,   four,   Ben-ny's   at   the   kitch-en   door,
2. Do,   re,   mi,   fa,   Now he wants some more, ha-ha!

Five,   six,   sev'n,   eight,   Eat-ing cher-ries off the plate.
So,   la,   ti,   do,   Moth-er says to him, "No, no!"

One and Two Are Three

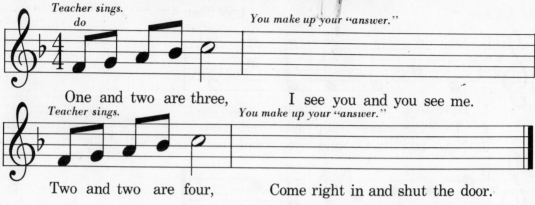

Teacher sings.
do

You make up your "answer."

One and two are three,   I see you and you see me.

Teacher sings.   *You make up your "answer."*

Two and two are four,   Come right in and shut the door.

How many rhymes and songs can you make with numbers?

Ten Green Bottles

Traditional

so

There are ten green bot-tles · hang-ing on the wall,

Ten green bot-tles · hang-ing on the wall;

And if one green bot-tle should ac-ci-den-t'ly fall

There'd be nine green bot-tles a-hang-ing on the wall.

Keep on singing stanzas for 9, 8, 7, 6, 5, 4, 3, 2, 1, until there are "no green bottles a-hanging on the wall."

Six Little Dogs

Christine Turner Curtis

Puerto Rican

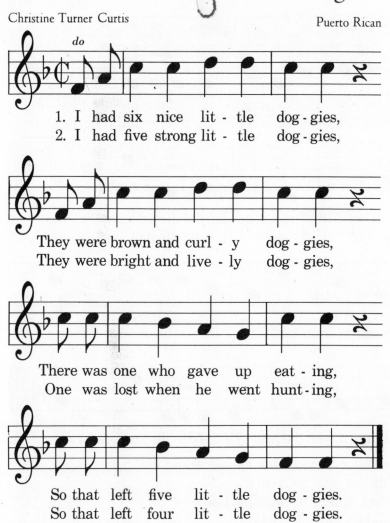

1. I had six nice lit - tle dog - gies,
2. I had five strong lit - tle dog - gies,

They were brown and curl - y dog - gies,
They were bright and live - ly dog - gies,

There was one who gave up eat - ing,
One was lost when he went hunt - ing,

So that left five lit - tle dog - gies.
So that left four lit - tle dog - gies.

3. I had four plump little doggies,
   They were smooth and silky doggies,
   One was frightened by a June bug,
   So that left three little doggies.

4. I had three cute little doggies,
   They were round and brown-eyed doggies,
   There was one went to the theater,
   So that left two little doggies.

5. I had two stout little doggies,
   They were gay and frisky doggies,
   There was one who climbed a nut tree,
   So that left one little doggie.

6. I had one nice little doggie,
   But my dog went up the mountain,
   And his name I have forgotten,
   So my story now is ended.

33

The Tailor and the Mouse

English Folk Song

1. There was a tai-lor had a mouse, Hi did-dle un-kum fee-dle.
2. The tai-lor thought the mouse was ill; Hi did-dle un-kum fee-dle.

They lived to-geth-er in one house, Hi did-dle un-kum fee-dle.
He gave him part of a blue pill, Hi did-dle un-kum fee-dle.

1,2,3,4. Hi did-dle un-kum ta-rum tan-tum, In the town of Ram-say,

Hi did-dle un-kum, o-ver the lea, Hi did-dle un-kum fee-dle.

3. The tailor thought his mouse would die;
Hi diddle unkum feedle.
He baked him in an apple pie,
Hi diddle unkum feedle.

4. The pie was cut, the mouse ran out,
Hi diddle unkum feedle.
The tailor followed him all about,
Hi diddle unkum feedle.

A Cat Came Fiddling

Traditional   Henry M. Halvorson

so   do   ti   la   so   mi   mi   fa   so

A   cat came fid-dling out of a barn,

With a   pair of bag-pipes un-der her arm;

She sang noth-ing but   "Fid-dle-dee - dee,

The mouse has mar-ried the bum-ble bee."

Play,   Cat!   Dance, Mouse! We'll have a wed-ding at our house.

Workaday Songs

Each singing what belongs to him or her
and to none else,
Singing with open mouths their strong,
melodious songs.

Walt Whitman

Haying Time

Translated by Leonard Borowicz

Polish Folk Song

do re mi fa so do la ti do la la so

1. On a Mon-day morn - ing Fa-ther mowed the hay.
2. On a Tues-day morn - ing Fa-ther raked the hay.
3. On a Wednes-day morn - ing Fa-ther dried the hay.

Fa-ther mowed and so did I, Both of us did mow the hay,
Fa-ther raked and so did I, Both of us did rake the hay,
Fa-ther dried and so did I, Both of us did dry the hay,

Fa-ther mowed and so did I, Both of us did mow the hay.
Fa-ther raked and so did I, Both of us did rake the hay.
Fa-ther dried and so did I, Both of us did dry the hay.

4. On a Thursday morning
   Father turned the hay.

5. On a Friday morning
   Father stacked the hay.

6. On a Saturday morning
   Father baled the hay.

7. On a Sunday morning
   Cows did eat the hay.

   Father saw them, so did I,
   Saw the cows that ate the hay.

Listen to "Wheelbarrow Motive," Anderson. (Victor Rhythm Album One.) How
many kinds of work motions can you make to this music?

Donkey Riding

Stevedore Song

do re mi mi fa re mi

1. Were you ev - er in Que-bec, Stow-ing tim-ber on the deck?
2. Were you ev - er off the Horn, Where it's al-ways fine and warm?

Where there's a King with a gold-en crown, Rid-ing on a don - key.
And seen the lion and the u - ni-corn, Rid-ing on a don - key.

CHORUS

la so so fa so mi

Hey! Ho! A - way we go! Don-key rid - ing, don-key rid - ing,

Hey! Ho! A - way we go! Rid - ing on a don - key.

3. Were you ever in Cardiff Bay,
   Where the folks all shout, "Hooray?"
   Here comes John with his three months' pay,
   Riding on a donkey.

This song was sung aboard the lumber boats sailing between Quebec and Liverpool. Singing it helped the crew stow the lumber on the deck. "Donkey riding" refers to the donkey-engine.

Home on the Range

Cowboy Song

Oh, give me a home where the buf - fa - lo roam,

Where the deer and the an - te - lope play, .

Where sel - dom is heard a dis - cour - ag - ing word,

And the skies are not cloud - y all day. .

Home, home on the range·Where the deer and the an - te - lope play,

Where sel-dom is heard a dis - cour-ag - ing word,

And the skies are not cloud - y all day. ·

Learning to Knit

V. M. S.

Verna Meade Surer

so la so mi re do mi so

1. Learn-ing to knit is. lots of fun, You put on two, then take off one.
2. Fast-er and fast - er, on I go. I love to sit and watch it grow.

Miss-ing a stitch and back you go, And then you start an - oth - er row.
On - ly one thing that puz-zles me, When I get through what will it be?

Haul Away, Joe

Sea Chantey

SOLO

so   do   do   do   so   mi   fa   fa   mi   re   mi   fa   so

1. A - way, haul a - way, · Come haul a - way to - geth - er,
2. A - way, haul a - way, · I'll sing to you of Nan - cy,

CHORUS

A - way, haul a - way, · Haul a - way, Joe.

SOLO

A - way, haul a - way, · We'll haul for fin - er weath - er,
A - way, haul a - way, · She's just my style and fan - cy,

CHORUS

A - way, haul a - way, · We'll haul a - way, Joe.

Singing Games

Can you dance?
I love to dance!
Music is my happy chance.
Music playing
In the street
Gets into
My hands and feet.

Eleanor Farjeon[1]

Turn, Cinnamon, Turn

Florida Singing Game

All up and down, my hon - ey, All up and down we go.

That la - dy's a-rock - in' her sug-ar-lump,

That la - dy's a-rock - in' her sug-ar-lump,

That la - dy's a - rock - in' her sug-ar-lump, Oh, turn, Cin-na-mon, turn!

The directions for playing these games are in your teacher's book.
She will show you how to play them.

[1]Reprinted by permission of the publishers, J. B. Lippincott Company, from *Sing for Your Supper* by Eleanor Farjeon. Copyright, 1938, by Eleanor Farjeon.

Shoemaker Dance

Danish Folk Game

Roll and roll the thread, oh, roll and roll the thread

And pull and pull and tap, tap, tap.

Roll and roll the thread, oh, roll and roll the thread

And pull and pull and tap, tap, tap.

One, two, three, hop, pol-ka so; One, two, three, a-way we go.

One, two, three, hop, pol-ka so; One, two, three, a-way we go.

High, Betty Martin

American Square Dance Song

High, · Bet-ty Mar-tin, tip toe, tip toe,

High, · Bet-ty Mar-tin, tip toe fine.

Nev-er found a boy to suit her fan-cy,

Nev-er found a boy to suit her mind.

Tra la la la la la la la, Tra la la la la la la la,

Tra la la la, Bet-ty Mar-tin, please be mine.

Skip to My Lou

Traditional Singing Game

mi   do   mi   so   re   ti   re   fa

1. Lost my part-ner, what will I do; Lost my part-ner, what will I do;

Lost my part-ner, what will I do? Skip to my Lou, my dar - ling.

CHORUS

Skip, skip, skip to my Lou; Skip, skip, skip to my Lou;

Skip, skip, skip to my Lou; Skip to my Lou, my dar - ling.

2. I'll get another one, better than you.
3. Can't get a red bird, a blue bird will do.
4. Little red wagon, painted blue.
5. Fly in the sugar bowl, shoo, shoo, shoo.

The Needle's Eye

American Singing Game

do

Oh, the nee-dle's eye that doth sup-ply The thread that runs so tru - ly,

There is man-y a lass that I let pass, Be-cause I want-ed you.
(There is man-y a beau that I let go, Be-cause I want-ed you.)

mi so so la la so

Be-cause I want-ed you, · Be-cause I want-ed you. ·

There's man-y a lass that I let pass, Be-cause I want-ed you. ·
(beau) (go)

so do so

You, you, you. · Be - cause I want - ed you. ·

45

Here Sits a Monkey

Mississippi Singing Game

so

1. Oh, here sits a mon-key in the chair, chair, chair,
2. Oh, here sits a don-key in the chair, chair, chair,

1,2. She lost all the true loves she had last year.
(He)   (he)

Oh, rise up-on your feet and greet the first you meet,

|1| |2|

The best-look-ing girl I know. know.
(boy)

Oats and Beans and Barley Grow

Singing Game

mi   fa

Oats and beans and bar-ley grow, Oats and beans and bar-ley grow,
Thus the farm-er sows his seed, Thus he stands and takes his ease,

Can you or I or an-y-one know, How oats and beans and bar-ley grow?
Then stamps his foot and claps · his hands And turns a-round and views the land.

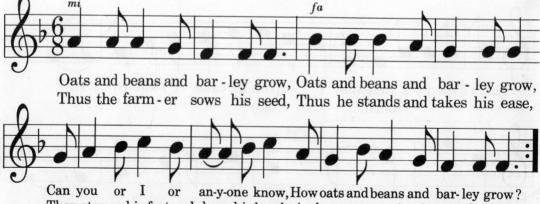

46

CHORUS

Wait - ing for a part - ner, Wait - ing for a part - ner,

O-pen the ring and choose one in While we all gai - ly dance and sing.

In Elvas

Translated by Christine Turner Curtis

Portuguese Singing Game

mi

1. In El - vas, in El - vas, when last I was there, In-
Chorus: Sweet girl in the ring, I ad - vise you to scur - ry; You'll
(Sweet boy)

es drank her cof - fee out - side in the air.
be all a - lone if you're not in a hur - ry.

2. "I'd like just a sip of your coffee today."
   Inés shook her head, "Will you please run and play?"

Chorus: Sweet girl in the ring, I advise you to scurry;
You'll be all alone if you're not in a hurry.

Chickama, Chickama, Craney-Crow

Southern Singing Game

do   *mi*   *so*   *re*   *so*

1. Chick-a-ma, chick-a-ma, cran-ey-crow, I went to the well to wash my toe.
2. Chick-a-ma, chick-a-ma, cran-ey-crow, I went to the well to wash my toe.

Spoken

When I got back one chick-en was gone. What's the time, old witch? One o'-clock.
When I got back two chick-ens were gone. What's the time, old witch? Two o'-clock.

Buoy, Buoy[1]

Translated by Cecil Cowdrey

Portuguese Singing Game

so

Fish - er bu - oy bob - bing, You go like this, like this!

Boys move like a buoy rocking on the waves.

When the tide is run - ning, You bob like this, like this!

Lit-tle seam-stress, as you sew your seam, Now do like this, like this!

Girls pretend to sew.

Lit-tle seam-stress, as you sew your seam, Now do like this, like this!

[1] Pronounce boo-ee

Brothers, Let Us Dance

Katherine S. Bolt

Dance of the Warm Spring Indians from Oregon

1. Broth-ers, let us dance; Beat up-on the drum.
2. We will stamp our feet, Bend our heads down low,

Make the cir-cle wid-er, wid-er! Here we come.
Lift our knees up high-er, high-er! Here we go.

I See You

Swedish Singing Game

I see you, I see you, Tra la la la la la la la la!

I see you, I see you, Tra la la la la la la la la!

You see me and I see you, And you take me and I take you.

You see me and I see you, And you take me and I take you.

On the Ground Here I Lie

Chippewa Indian Song

On the ground here I lie, Face to earth as I cry.

That bad boy's noth-ing to me, Why should I an-gry be?
(girl's)

Charles J. Cromwell

Rosa

Flemish Dance Tune

mi fa re do | Fine

1. Ro - sa, come to the par - ty, the par - ty, the par - ty,
2. Ro - sa, come to the par - ty, the par - ty, the par - ty,

Ro - sa, come to the par - ty and dance with me.
Ro - sa, come to the par - ty and dance with me.

Lit - tle girl from for-eign land, Don't you think our coun-try's grand?
Lit - tle girl from o'er the sea, Wel-come to our coun - try free.

D.C. al Fine

We wel - come you.
We wel - come you.

King William

Southern Game Song

so do do do so la la so

1. King Wil-liam was King James-'s son, And he the roy-al race did run,
2. Go forth to east, go forth to west, Go choose the one that you love best,
3. Now rise and stand on your two feet, And greet your true love, greet your sweet,

He wore a star up - on his breast, It point-ed east, it point-ed west.
Down on the car - pet you must kneel, And tell the whole world how you feel.
Then take your part-ner from the ring, While once a - gain we dance and sing.

Old Roger Is Dead

English Singing Game

so   do

1. Old   Rog - er   is dead,   and   gone   to   his grave;
2. Three ap - ple trees grew   up   o - ver his head;
3. The   ap - ples were ripe   and   read - y   to drop;

Ho   hum,   gone   to   his   grave.
Ho   hum,   o - ver   his   head.
Ho   hum,   read - y   to   drop.

4. There came an east wind a-blowing them off;
   Ho hum, blowing them off.

5. There came an old woman a-picking them up;
   Ho hum, picking them up.

6. Old Roger jumped up and gave her a knock;
   Ho hum, gave her a knock.

7. Which made the old woman go hippity hop;
   Ho hum, hippity hop.

51

People We Like to Know

Over on the corner
The balloon man stands,
Holding fast the slender threads,
Wound around his hands.

Balls of royal purple,
Balls of brilliant blue,
Gleaming reds and yellows,
Nod their heads to you.

The Oil Station Man

Jack Sutton

so   so   do   re   ti   la

1. Oh, the oil sta-tion man is our friend, friend, friend.
2. And now on our bikes we will ride, ride, ride,

Our bi - cy - cle tires he'll mend, mend, mend.
A - rac - ing, a - rac - ing side by side.

He puts on a patch and sizz, sizz, sizz,
The oil sta - tion man just smiles, smiles, smiles,

He blows up our tires and a - way we whizz.
As mer - ri - ly on we ride for miles.

The Tamale Man

Joan Henry

"Hot ta-ma-les, · hot ta-ma-les," · the ta-ma-le man calls to - day.

The ta-ma-le man calls this way, "Hot ta-ma-les, · hot ta-ma-les."

The Lamplighter

Translated by Cecil Cowdrey

Spanish Folk Song

1. Up and down the cit - y streets at fall of night,
2. Past the dark-ened win-dows where the road is steep,

With my lad - der tall I go, my lamps to light. ·
As I light my lamps with care, the count I keep. ·

3. Two and four are six, and two are now eight more.
   Eight and eight, sixteen, and eight make twenty-four.

4. Twenty-four and eight make thirty-two, I say.
   Now beside the chapel door I kneel and pray.

Flowers For Sale

Marian Deere

Flow'rs for sale, Flow'rs for sale, Love-ly blue vi-o-lets,

Sweet yel-low daf-fo-dils, Pan-sies and but-ter-cups.

Who'll buy my flow'rs? Flow'rs for sale, Flow'rs for sale.

Will You Buy?

Christine Turner Curtis

French Market Song

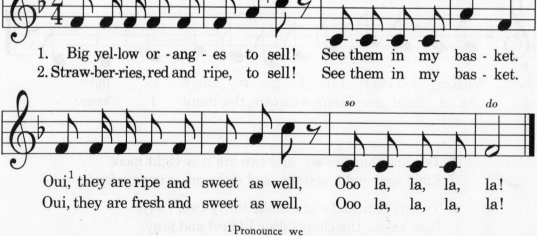

1. Big yel-low or-ang-es to sell! See them in my bas-ket.
2. Straw-ber-ries, red and ripe, to sell! See them in my bas-ket.

Oui,[1] they are ripe and sweet as well, Ooo la, la, la, la!
Oui, they are fresh and sweet as well, Ooo la, la, la, la!

¹Pronounce we

Songland People

Susie, Little Susie

Translated from the German

German Folk Song
from "Hänsel and Gretel"

1. Su - sie, lit - tle Su - sie, now what is the news?
2. Su - sie, lit - tle Su - sie, we are in a fix,

The geese are go - ing bare - foot be - cause they've no shoes.
No pen - nies for some sug - ar and no bread to mix.

The cob - bler has leath - er, but no last to use,
If I sell my bed, sleep on straw for the night,

So he can - not make them a pair of new shoes.
Feath - ers will not prick - le and fleas will not bite.

Listen to "Susie, Little Susie," Humperdinck. (Victor Listening Album Four.)

Polly-Wolly-Doodle

College Song

1. Oh, I went down South to see my Sal,
2. Oh, my Sal - ly is a maid - en fair,

Sing Pol - ly - wol - ly - doo - dle all the day;
Sing Pol - ly - wol - ly - doo - dle all the day;

My · Sal - ly is a spunk - y gal,
With · curl - y eyes and laugh - ing hair,

Sing Pol - ly - wol - ly - doo - dle all the day.
Sing Pol - ly - wol - ly - doo - dle all the day.

56

CHORUS

Fare thee well, fare thee well, Fare thee well, my fair - y fay,

For I'm going to Loui-si - an - a, for to see my Su - sy - an - na,

Sing Pol - ly - wol - ly - doo - dle all the day.

3. Behind the barn, down on my knees,
Sing Polly-wolly-doodle all the day,
I thought I heard a chicken sneeze,
Sing Polly-wolly-doodle all the day.

4. He sneezed so hard with whooping cough,
Sing Polly-wolly-doodle all the day,
He sneezed his head and tail right off,
Sing Polly-wolly-doodle all the day.

Adapted from
Mother Goose

Tom, Tom, the Piper's Son

Children's Song

do

Tom, Tom, the pip - er's son, Stole a pig, and a - way he run;

The pig got loose and stole a goose, And Tom got put in the cal - a - boose.

57

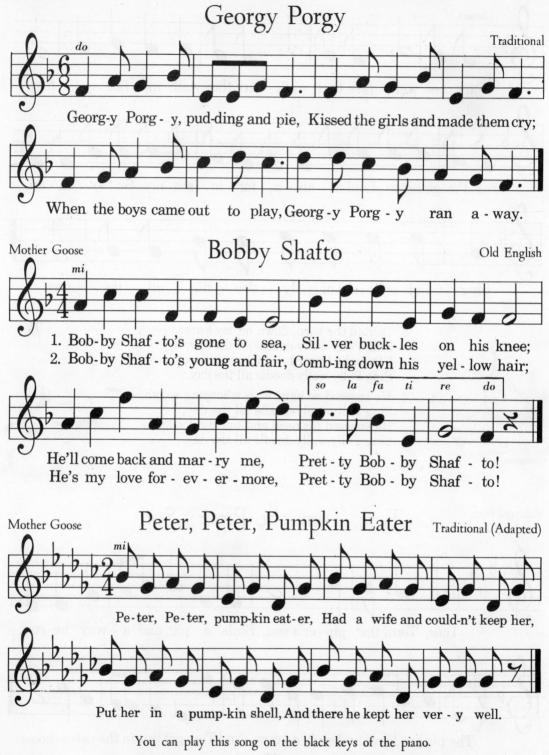

Georgy Porgy

Traditional

do

Georg-y Porg-y, pud-ding and pie, Kissed the girls and made them cry;

When the boys came out to play, Georg-y Porg-y ran a-way.

Bobby Shafto

Mother Goose

Old English

mi

1. Bob-by Shaf-to's gone to sea, Sil-ver buck-les on his knee;
2. Bob-by Shaf-to's young and fair, Comb-ing down his yel-low hair;

so la fa ti re do

He'll come back and mar-ry me, Pret-ty Bob-by Shaf-to!
He's my love for-ev-er-more, Pret-ty Bob-by Shaf-to!

Peter, Peter, Pumpkin Eater

Mother Goose

Traditional (Adapted)

mi

Pe-ter, Pe-ter, pump-kin eat-er, Had a wife and could-n't keep her,

Put her in a pump-kin shell, And there he kept her ver-y well.

You can play this song on the black keys of the piano.

Home and Family

She loves me when I'm glad er sad;
She loves me when I'm good er bad.

An' when my Pa comes home to tea,
She loves him 'most as much as me.

James Whitcomb Riley

Nobody Knows But Mother

Mary Morrison

Peter Dalton

Solo

1. How man-y but-tons are miss-ing to-day?
2. How man-y mud-dy shoes all in a row?
3. How man-y lunch-es for Tom-my and Sam?

Class

No-bod-y knows but moth-er.
No-bod-y knows but moth-er.
No-bod-y knows but moth-er.

How man-y play-things are strewn in her way?
How man-y stock-ings to darn, do you know?
Cook-ies and ap-ples and black-ber-ry jam?

No-bod-y knows but moth-er.
No-bod-y knows but moth-er.
No-bod-y knows but moth-er.

59

Helping Mother Bake a Cake

V. M. S.

Verna Meade Surer

Help-ing moth-er bake a cake we think is fun,

It looks so good we can hard-ly wait till the bak-ing's done.

Drop in the eggs then beat, beat, beat, Now add the sug-ar to make it sweet,

Sift the flour, then add the milk, Stir, stir, stir, till it's soft as silk.

Beat once more with all your might, Just to be sure it's fluff-y and light;

Pour in the pan and bake, bake, bake. Yum, yum, yum, can't you taste the cake?

Mother and Baby

Translated by Johanna C. F. Auer
Paraphrase by Susanna Myers

J. P. J. Wierts

so   so   la   ti   do   ti   la   so   mi   so

1. Our ba - by is snug in his cra - dle warm,   And
2. When ba - by wakes up from his morn - ing nap,   As

Moth-er is sit-ting close by. · She hums a gen - tle,
hap-py and sweet as can be, · And Moth - er lifts him

sleep - y song, Her knit - ting nee - dles fly. ·
in her arms His smile is love -ly to see. ·

Rock - a - by, O rock - a - by, Hush, hush, cos - i - ly rock-ing,
Moth-er dear; O Moth - er dear, I love you and our ba - by,

Rock - a - by, O rock - a - by,
Moth - er dear, O Moth - er dear,

Hush - a - by, ba - by, your cra - dle is warm.
Here are ten kiss - es from ba - by and me.

The Cupboard

Walter de la Mare

Jacques Armin

so do do so so la mi | mi mi fa fa so so do

1. I know a lit - tle cup - board, with a tee - ny ti - ny key,
2. I have a small, fat grand-ma-ma, with a ver - y slip-p'ry knee,

And there's a jar of Lol - ly-pops for me, me, me.
She's Keep - er of the Cup-board, with the key, key, key.

It has a lit - tle shelf, my dear, As dark as dark can be,
And when I'm ver - y good, my dear, As good as good can be,

And there's a dish of Ban-bur-y Cakes for me, me, me.
There's Ban-bur-y Cakes and Lol - ly-pops for me, me, me.

Grandfather's Song

Victor Hugo
Translated by Christine Turner Curtis

A. Marmontel

do   so   so   so   la   so fa so   mi   re   re   mi   do

1. Dance, grand-daugh-ters, dance, my dar-lings, dance in the spring.
2. Dance, my beau-ties, while grand-fa-ther nods in his chair.

All the trees will laugh to see you turn in a ring.
Birds will clap their wings to see you, high in the air.

Dance a-way the care-less morn-ing, hour aft-er hour.
Dance, my dar-lings, crowned with hare-bells, blue as the skies.

Dance un-til your new lit-tle school-books burst in-to flow'r.
Dance with sun-rise on your·cheeks and dawn in your eyes.

Don't Want to Go Home

English version by Fjeril Hess

Czech Children's Song

do do do ti so

Don't want to go home, don't want to go home, Moth-er's cross with me.

Don't want to go home, don't want to go home, Moth-er's cross with me.

do mi mi so so fa re

Took her ap - ple pie, you see, She'll put me a - cross her knee.

Don't want to go home, don't want to go home, Moth-er's cross with me.

Klein, Klein Kleuterken (Little Mischief)

Translated by Carol Fuller

Netherlands Folk Song

so do

Klein, klein Kleu - ter - ken, You picked my flow'rs to - day!

In gar-den beds you pulled their heads, You left no -bud to stay,

So I must tell your fa - ther, And then what will he say?

Klein, klein Kleu - ter - ken, You picked my flow'rs to - day!

Old Folks at Home

Stephen Collins Foster

Way down up - on the Swa-nee Riv - er, Far, far a - way,
All up and down the whole cre - a - tion Sad - ly I roam,

There's where my heart is turn-ing ev - er, There's where the old folks stay.
Still long-ing for the old plan-ta-tion, And for the old folks at home.

All the world is sad and drear-y Ev - 'ry-where I roam;

O loved ones, how my heart grows wea-ry, Far from the old folks at home.

Getting Up and Going to Bed

I Wake In the Morning

Rose Fyleman

Lydia Elwood

I wake in the morn-ing ear-ly, And al-ways the ver-y first thing,

I poke out my head and I sit up in bed And I sing, sing, sing.

Morning Song

Translated by Margareta Wassali

Swiss Folk Song

1. The sun is shin-ing bright-ly, Get up, Kat-ter-lin,
2. The rab-bits jump and scam-per, Get up, Kat-ter-lin,

The birds are sing-ing sweet-ly, Get up, Kat-ter-lin.
The cows are in the pas-ture, Get up, Kat-ter-lin.

1, 2. Hur - ry up, out of bed, Time for break-fast, sleep - y - head.

Ding - a - ling - a - ling - a - ling. Get up, sleep - y - head.

I Yawn So

Jack Sutton

so *do* *re* *so* *mi*

At night when it's time for my bed · I yawn so; ·
(Small yawn.)

Then Moth-er says, "Cov-er your mouth · and yawn so." ·
(Yawn politely.)

But some-times I'm sure to for - get · and yawn so,
(Big yawn.)

YAWN · SO! · ·
(Great big yawn and stretch.)

67

Little Child, Good Child

Fannie Stearns Davis

Henry M. Halvorson

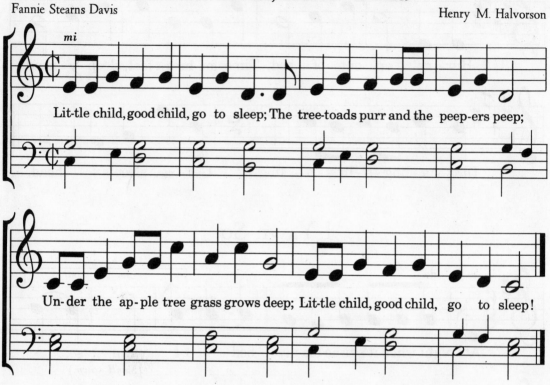

Lit-tle child, good child, go to sleep; The tree-toads purr and the peep-ers peep;

Un-der the ap-ple tree grass grows deep; Lit-tle child, good child, go to sleep!

How many of you can play this piece on the piano, using both hands?

Lullaby

Johannes Brahms

Watch these notes as you listen to the record. (Victor Listening Album One.)

Slumber Song

Translated

Chilean Lullaby

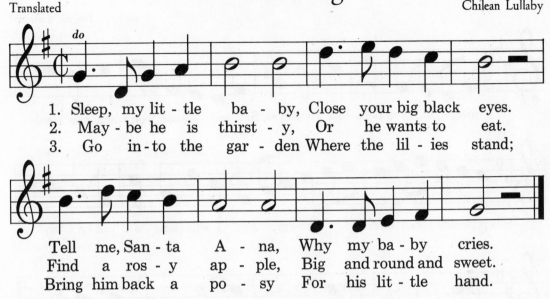

1. Sleep, my lit - tle   ba - by, Close your big black   eyes.
2. May - be he is thirst - y, Or   he wants to   eat.
3. Go in-to the   gar - den Where the lil - ies   stand;

Tell   me, San - ta   A - na, Why my ba - by   cries.
Find a ros - y   ap - ple, Big and round and sweet.
Bring him back a   po - sy For his lit - tle   hand.

Listen to "Sleeping Time," Pinto. (Victor Listening Album One.)

Eskimo Baby

E. S. D.

Esther S. Duncan

Go to sleep, Es - ki - mo ba - by, · Cold is the night, and long!

Warm is your ig - loo shel-ter, · And I'll sing you this slum-ber song!

pp slowly

Oo · · · mm.

69

Golden Slumbers

English Lullaby

Gold - en slum-bers kiss your eyes, Smiles · a-wait you when you rise;

Sleep, pret-ty loved one, do · not cry, And I will sing a lull - a - by,

Lull - a - by, lull - a - by, lull - a - by.

Moses in the Bulrushes

Southern Religious Ballad

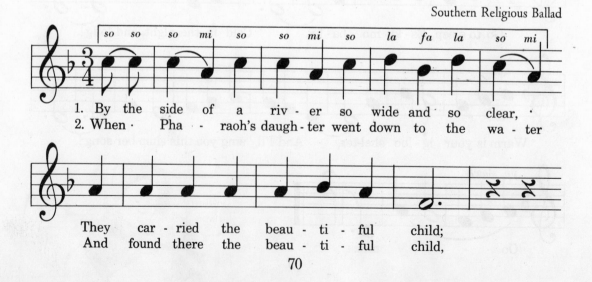

1. By the side of a riv - er so wide and · so clear, ·
2. When · Pha - raoh's daugh - ter went down to the wa - ter

They car - ried the beau - ti - ful child;
And found there the beau - ti - ful child,

70

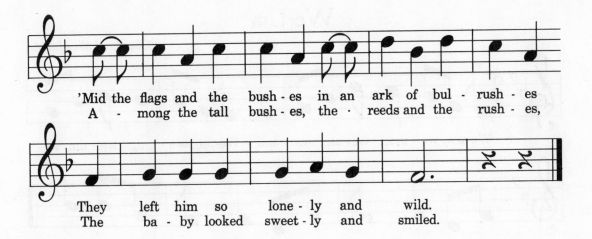

'Mid the flags and the bush-es in an ark of bul-rush-es
A - mong the tall bush-es, the reeds and the rush-es,

They left him so lone-ly and wild.
The ba-by looked sweet-ly and smiled.

What Will We Do With the Baby-O?

American Folk Song

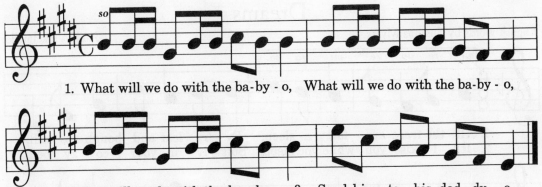

1. What will we do with the ba-by - o, What will we do with the ba-by - o,

What will we do with the ba-by - o? Send him to his dad-dy - o.

2. Wind blows high and the wind blows low,
   Where, oh where does the old wind go?
   What will we do with the baby-o?
   Send him to his daddy-o.

3. Down in the hollow the cowbells ring,
   Bullfrogs jump and the jay-bird sings.
   What will we do with the baby-o?
   Send him to his daddy-o.

4. Bullfrog croaked and jumped up high,
   Jumped and jumped 'til he caught a fly
   What will we do with the baby-o?
   Send him to his daddy-o.

71

We-Um

Cherokee Indian Lullaby

We-um, we-um, we-um, we-um, We-um, we-um, we-um, we-um, we-um, We-um, we-um, we-um, we-um.

You can play this song on the black keys of the piano if you start on the black key above Middle C.

Dreams

English words by Susanna Myers

Paul Winkelmüller

1. All the trees are fast a-sleep, Ev-'ry leaf and bough are still,
2. If I kiss you while you sleep, Soft-ly in your co-zy bed,

Dreams come drift-ing through the night, While the moon sails o'er the hill.
Hap-py dreams will quick-ly come To your gold-en, sleep-y head.

Sleep, my lit-tle ba-by, Sleep, my ba-by dear. ·
Sleep, my lit-tle ba-by, Sleep, my ba-by dear. ·

Listen to "Sweet and Low," Barnby. (Victor Listening Album One.)

Songs of Devotion

Make a joyful noise unto the Lord, all ye lands.
Serve the Lord with gladness:
Come before His presence with singing.

Psalm 100

Father, Lead Me Day by Day

John P. Hopps

George C. Strattner

Fa-ther, lead me day by day, Ev-er in Thine own strong way;

Teach me to be pure and true, Show me what I ought to do.

Come, Thou Almighty King

Felice de Giardini

Anonymous

Come, Thou al - might - y King, Help us Thy Name to sing,

Help us to praise! Fa-ther, all - glo - ri - ous, O'er all vic - to - ri - ous,

Come and reign o - ver us, An - cient of Days.

Children of the Heavenly King

John Cennick

Ignaz J. Pleyel

Chil-dren of the heav'n-ly King, As ye jour-ney, sweet-ly sing;

Sing your Sav-iour's worth-y praise, Glo-rious in His works and ways.

Swing Low, Sweet Chariot

Negro Spiritual

Swing low, sweet char-i-ot, · Com-ing for to car-ry me home,

· Swing low, sweet char-i-ot, · Com-ing for to car-ry me home.

An Evening Hymn

Thomas Ken

Thomas Tallis

All praise to Thee, my God, this night, For all the bless-ings of the light!

Keep me, O keep me, King of kings, Be-neath Thy own al-might-y wings!

Crusaders' Hymn

Anonymous

Silesian Folk Song

do   do   do   re   ti   do   *mi   mi   mi   fa   re   mi*

1. Fair are the mead - ows,   Fair - er the wood - lands,
2. Fair is the sun - shine,   Fair - er the moon - light,

Robed in flow'rs of bloom - ing spring;
And the spar - kling stars on high;

Je - sus is fair - er;   Je - sus is pur - er;
Je - sus shines bright - er,   Je - sus shines pur - er

He makes our sor - r'wing spir - it sing.
Than all the an - gels in the sky.

About Happy Holidays

Come with laughter and hooraying,
Fling your heels a-holidaying.

Nancy Birckhead

Birthday

Birthday Song

Frances B. Martin

mi   so   re   mi   do   so

This is Ma-ry's birth-day! Hap-py Birth-day to you!
Bil - ly's

Hap-py Birth-day to you! This is Ma-ry's birth - day!
Bil - ly's

Hap-py Birth-day, Hap-py Birth-day to you!

My Friend John

Translated by Susanna Myers

Brittany Dance Song

Sing hel - lo to · hap-py John! Here he comes, do you see him smil-ing?
(Jane) (she) (her)

My friend John, my good friend John With a smile you can see a mile!
(Jane) (Jane)

I feel sure he got a pres-ent, Some-thing nice has made him smile,
(she) (her)

Yes, I'm sure to - day's his birth-day, With that smile you can see a mile.
(her)

For other verses, use other names.

Columbus Day

Columbus

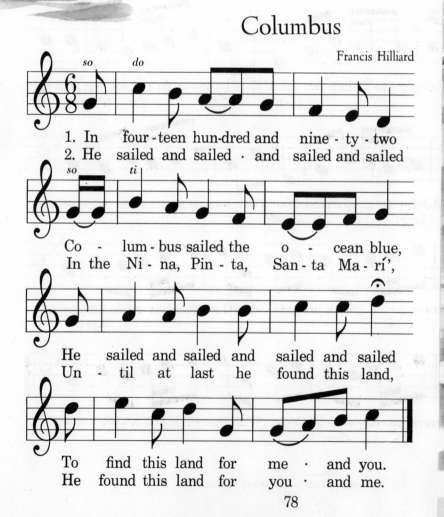

Francis Hilliard

so   *do*

1. In four-teen hun-dred and nine-ty-two
2. He sailed and sailed · and sailed and sailed

so   *ti*

Co - lum - bus sailed the o - cean blue,
In the Ni - na, Pin - ta, San - ta Ma - rí',

He sailed and sailed and sailed and sailed
Un - til at last he found this land,

To find this land for me · and you.
He found this land for you · and me.

Halloween

The dogs bark,
The night is dark,
And spooky things are seen.
The witches ride,
The children hide,
Tonight is Halloween.

Arthur Findley

Soon Comes the Day

Velma Hanlin

do ti la   re ti so

Soon comes the day we call Hal - low - een.

Fun - ni - est fac - es you've ev - er seen;

Pump-kins and cook-ies and ap - ples too.

Oh, we all like Hal - low - een.

Listen to "March of the Dwarfs," Grieg. (Victor Listening Album Three.)

Five Little Pumpkins

Unknown   L. B. P.

so

Five   lit - tle pump - kins   sit - ting on   a   gate,

do

The   first   one   said,   "Oh   my, it's get - ting late."

re

The   sec - ond one said, "There are witch - es in the air."

mi

The   third   one   said,   "But   we   don't care."

fa

The fourth   one   said, "Let's run and run and run."

so

The   fifth   one   said, "I'm   read - y for some fun."

80

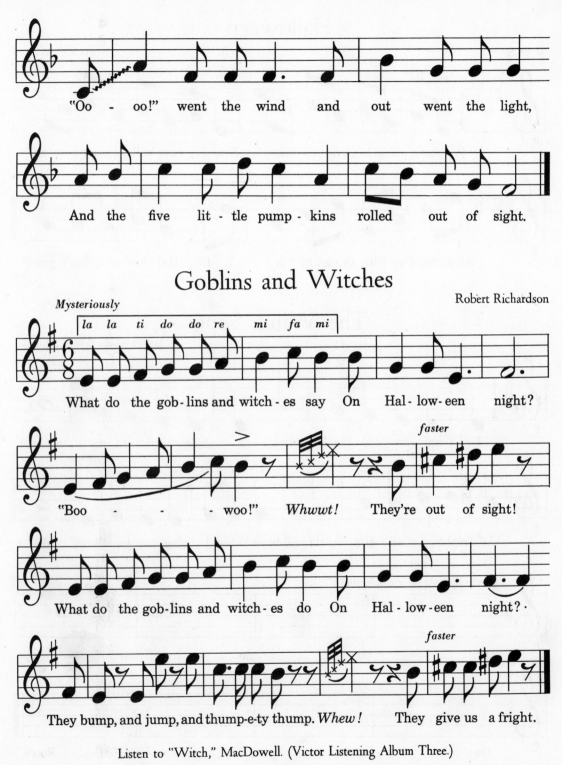

"Oo - oo!" went the wind and out went the light,

And the five lit-tle pump-kins rolled out of sight.

Goblins and Witches

Robert Richardson

Mysteriously

la la ti do do re mi fa mi

What do the gob-lins and witch-es say On Hal-low-een night?

"Boo - - -woo!" *Whwwt!* They're out of sight!

What do the gob-lins and witch-es do On Hal-low-een night?·

They bump, and jump, and thump-e-ty thump. *Whew!* They give us a fright.

faster

Listen to "Witch," MacDowell. (Victor Listening Album Three.)

Halloween

V.M.S.

Verna Meade Surer

so *do*

Witch-es, pump-kins, fun-ny fac - es, Ring-ing door-bells, go-ing plac - es.

All dressed up with things to do.   I like Hal - low - een, don't you?

The Witch Song

Jeffersonville School Children

I   am an old black witch!   I   ride up - on my   broom!

I fright-en all the   girls and boys When I   sing my lone-some   tune.

(Make up your own witch tune.)

Oo . . . . oo . . . . oo . . . . oo

Oo . . . . oo . . . . oo . . . . oo . . . Boo!

Thanksgiving

For father's care and mother's love,
For the blue sky and clouds above,
For springtime and autumn gay
We thank Thee this Thanksgiving Day!

Mattie M. Renwick

Thanksgiving

Ralph Waldo Emerson

John Langland

so *do*

For each new morn-ing with its light, Fa - ther, we thank Thee.

For rest and shel-ter of the night, Fa - ther, we thank Thee.

For health and food, for love of friends, For ev-'ry-thing Thy good-ness sends,

Fa - ther in Heav'n, we thank Thee.

83

Gobble, Gobble, Gobble

Margaret I. Simpson

June M. Norton

A tur-key sat on a back-yard fence And he sang this sad, sad tune,

"Thanks-giv-ing Day is com-ing, gob-ble, gob-ble, gob-ble, gob-ble,

And I know I'll be eat-en soon.

Gob-ble, gob-ble, gob-ble, gob-ble, gob-ble, gob-ble, gob-ble,

I would like to run a-way,

Gob-ble, gob-ble, gob-ble, gob-ble, gob-ble, gob-ble, gob-ble,

I don't like Thanks-giv-ing Day!"

Christmas

Sing hey! Sing hey!
For Christmas Day
Twine mistletoe and holly,

For friendship glows
In winter snows,
And so let's all be jolly.

Nursery Rhyme

Jolly Old Saint Nicholas

Traditional

mi

1. Jol - ly old Saint Nich - o - las, Lean your ear this way,
2. When the clock is strik-ing twelve, When I'm fast a - sleep,
3. John - ny wants a pair of skates, Su - sie needs a sled,

Don't you tell a sin - gle soul What I'm going to say.
Down the chim-ney with your pack, Soft - ly you will creep.
Nel - ly wants a sto - ry - book, One she has - n't read.

Christ-mas Eve will soon be here, Now, you dear old man,
All the stock-ings you will find, Hang-ing in a row;
As for me, I hard - ly know, So I'll go to rest;

Whis-per what you'll bring to me, Tell me if you can.
Mine will be the short - est one, You'll be sure to know.
Choose for me, dear San - ta Claus, What you think is best.

Listen to "March of the Toys," Tchaikovsky (Victor Rhythm Album Two) and "March of the Tin Soldiers," Tchaikovsky (Victor Rhythm Album Three).

Merry Christmas Bells

J.R.M.

James R. Murray

so

Mer - ry, mer - ry, mer - ry, mer - ry Christ - mas bells, Oh,

sweet - ly, sweet - ly chime; Let your hap - py voic - es through the

Fine

breez - es swell, This mer - ry, mer - ry Christ - mas time.

1. Peace on earth, good will to men, O an - gel voic - es, sing a - gain,
2. Ban - ish ev - 'ry thought of care, Let mirth and mu - sic fill the air,

D.C. al Fine

While hearts and voic - es once a - gain Join in the sweet re - frain.
While hearts and voic - es once a - gain Join in the sweet re - frain.

The First Noel

Old English Carol

mi re do re mi fa so la ti do ti la so

The · first · No - el, the · an - gels did say,

Was to cer - tain poor shep-herds in fields as they lay:

In · fields · where they lay · keep-ing their sheep

On a cold win-ter's night · that was · so deep.

No - el, · No - el, No - el, No - el,

Born is the King · of Is - ra - el.

Christmas

Puerto Rican School Child

do ti la so mi

Christ-mas is here! · Christ-mas is here! ·

All sing with joy! All sing with joy!

It's the mer-ry sea-son, It's the mer-ry sea-son

fa mi re do

When Christ was born, When Christ was born.

The Christmas Star

Marion K. Seavey

Gertrude E. McGunigle

so mi so do re mi so

O star of shin-ing beau-ty In the Christ-mas sky, ·

Long a-go you heard a ti-ny Ba-by's lull-a-by. ·

You shone in-to a man-ger And there up-on the hay .

You saw the Child Who gave the world Its first glad Christ-mas day. ·

Run, Neighbors, to the Crib

Translated by Susanna Myers

French Carol

1. Run, neigh-bors, to the crib, · To see the love-ly Child ·
2. All gifts we bring to Him · Be-cause we know His love

Who lies there on the straw, Dear Je-sus, gen-tle, mild;
Will help some oth-er child, And hon-or God a - bove.

He wins our faith-ful love, · As nev-er child be - fore. ·
Let mu-sic fill the air, · Old songs we love to sing, ·

Come, neigh-bors, kneel you down, · This heav'n-ly Child a - dore. ·
And oth-ers that are new, · In praise of heav-en's King. ·

Translated

Oh Come, Little Children

J. A. P. Schulz

1. Oh come, lit - tle chil - dren, Oh come, one and all,
2. Oh, see in the man - ger, In hal - low - ed light
3. Oh, there lies the Christ-Child On hay and on straw;

To Beth - le - hem's sta - ble, In Beth - le - hem's stall,
A star throws its beam On this ho - li - est sight.
The shep - herds are kneel - ing Be - fore Him with awe.

And see with re - joic - ing This glo - ri - ous sight,
In clean swad - dling clothes Lies the Heav - en - ly Child,
And Ma - ry and Jo - seph Smile on Him with love,

Our Fa - ther in Heav - en Has sent us this night.
More love - ly than an - gels This Ba - by so mild.
While an - gels are sing - ing Sweet songs from a - bove.

Hark! the Herald Angels Sing

Charles Wesley

Felix Mendelssohn

Hark! the her-ald an-gels sing, "Glo-ry to the new-born King!

Peace on earth, and mer-cy mild, · God and sin-ners re-con-ciled."

Joy-ful, all ye na-tions, rise, · Join the tri-umph of the skies;·

With th'an-gel-ic host pro-claim, "Christ is · born in Beth-le-hem."

Hark! the her-ald an-gels sing, "Glo-ry · to the new-born King!"

Perhaps you would like to sing this song with the record. (Christmas Album, Victor Basic Record Library.)

Pine Tree Song

Marjorie Barrows

Robert W. Gibb

so la do re mi so mi so

1. Lit - tle pines up - on the hill, Sleep-ing in · the moon-light still,
2. Now my arms, for girls and boys, Blos-som with · a hun-dred toys.

Are you dream-ing now of me Who bloomed in - to a Christ-mas tree?
O lit - tle pines, it's fun to live To be a Christ-mas tree and give.

O Little Town of Bethlehem

Phillips Brooks

Lewis H. Redner

mi

O lit - tle town of Beth - le - hem, How still we · see thee lie,

A - bove thy deep and dream-less sleep The si - lent stars go by;

Yet in thy dark streets shin - eth The ev - er - last - ing light;

The hopes and fears of all the years Are met in thee to - night.

(Christmas Album, Victor Basic Record Library.)

Valentine's Day

Saint Valentine's Day

Sally Bowen

Soon it will be Saint Val - en - tine's Day,

When our box will be o - pened and all will be gay.

Val - en - tines pret - ty, val - en - tines small,

Val - en - tines fun - ny, e - nough for us all.

Oh, how we love Saint Val - en - tine's Day,

When our box will be o - pened and all will be gay!

There came by the post
The loveliest thing
That one could imagine
A postman might bring!
It came to me
From a friend of mine,
It came to me
From my Valentine!

Elizabeth Winton

Roses Are Red

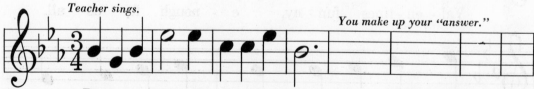

Teacher sings.   *You make up your "answer."*

Ros-es are red and vi-o-lets blue, Sug-ar is sweet and so are you.

Teacher sings.   *You make up your "answer."*

If you love me as I love you, No knife can cut our love in two.

Patriotic Days

Here was a man to hold against the world,
A man to match the mountains and the sea.

From "Lincoln, the Man of the People,"
by Edwin Markham

America the Beautiful

Katharine Lee Bates

Samuel A. Ward

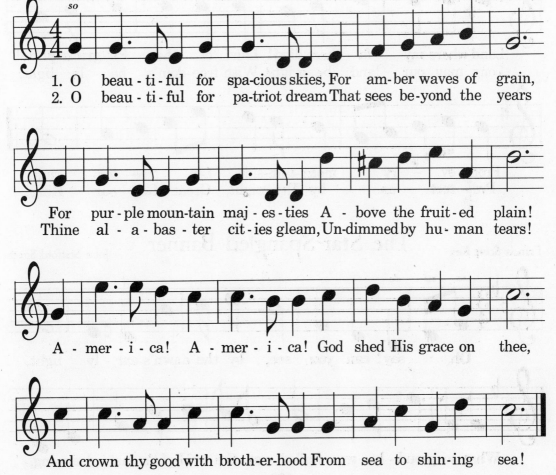

1. O beau-ti-ful for spa-cious skies, For am-ber waves of grain,
2. O beau-ti-ful for pa-triot dream That sees be-yond the years

For pur-ple moun-tain maj-es-ties A-bove the fruit-ed plain!
Thine al-a-bas-ter cit-ies gleam, Un-dimmed by hu-man tears!

A-mer-i-ca! A-mer-i-ca! God shed His grace on thee,

And crown thy good with broth-er-hood From sea to shin-ing sea!

Boy and soldier, in peace or strife,
He loved America all his life!

From "Washington,"
by Nancy Byrd Turner

America

Samuel Francis Smith

Traditional

1. My coun-try, 'tis of thee, Sweet land of lib - er -ty, Of thee I sing.
2. Our fa-thers' God! to Thee, Au - thor of lib - er -ty, To Thee we sing.

Land where my fa - thers died! Land of the Pil - grims' pride!
Long may our land be bright With free-dom's ho - ly light;

From ev - 'ry · moun-tain-side, Let free - dom ring!
Pro - tect us · by Thy might, Great God our King!

The Star-Spangled Banner

Francis Scott Key

John Stafford Smith

Oh, · say! can you see, by the dawn's ear - ly light,

What so proud - ly we hailed at the twi-light's last gleam-ing,

Easter

The Pealing Bells

1. I love to hear the peal-ing bells, the peal - ing bells.
2. Of East - er joy their peal-ing tells, their peal - ing tells.

Easter Bells

L. B. P.

East - er bells in church-es ring, Peo - ple in the church-es sing.

Ring-a-ling-a, ring-a-ling-a, ring-a-ling-a, ring; Sing-a-ling-a, sing-a-ling-a, sing-a-ling-a, sing.

Bim, bom, Bim bom bell.

Easter

Joyce Kilmer

Louise Giere

so

The air is like a but-ter-fly · With frail blue wings, ·

The hap - py earth looks at the sky · And sings, sings, sings.

A New Created World (from "Creation")

Franz Joseph Haydn

so *do*

A new cre - a - ted world, a · new cre - a - ted world

Springs up, springs up at · God's com - mand.

At Easter Time

Laura E. Richards

Ethel Anthony

so *la* *ti* *do* *re* *mi* *fa* *so*

1. The lit-tle flow'rs came thro' the ground At East-er time, at East-er time;
2. The pure white lil - y raised its cup At East-er time, at East-er time;

They raised their heads and looked a-round At hap - py East-er time.
The cro - cus to the sky looked up At hap - py East-er time.

At the Carnival

Oh, it's fun to dress up and go
To a great big carnival show
Where the funniest clowns do skip and prance
And merry-go-rounds play a kind of dance.

Merry-Go-Round

L. B. P.

Here we go gal - lop - ing round, Round and a-round and a - round,

Gal - lop-ing, gal - lop - ing round, Round and a-round and a - round.

See   our po - nies   go,   ·   Round the cir - cle   so.   ·

Sing and sing and   sing,   ·   Try   to catch   a   ring. ·

Gal - lop-ing, gal - lop-ing round, Now we jump off with a bound!

Mister Punchinello

Translated by Susanna Myers

French Children's Song

do

Knock! Who is there? It is Mis - ter Pun - chi - nel - lo.

Fine

Knock! Who is there? Pun - chi - nel - lo with his show!

1. He looks so fool - ish, He is a fun - ny fel - low,
2. When he is sing - ing You think he's on - ly jok - ing,

D.C. al Fine

But he is hap - py To hear you laugh, ho, ho!
But when he danc - es You shout and laugh, ho, ho!

The Funny Clown

E. A. B.

Ellen Arnott Bates

mi so fa mi fa so mi mi fa re re mi do do

The clown is such a fun-ny man, fun-ny man, fun-ny man;

The clown is such a fun-ny man, he laughs and laughs all day.

Ha, ha, ha, hee, hee, hee! Clowns are fun-ny as can be;

Ha, ha, ha, hee, hee, hee! Clowns are fun-ny as can be.

Listen to "Clown," MacDowell. (Victor Listening Album Three.)

ABOUT THE WONDERFUL
WORLD OUTSIDE

I'm glad the sky is painted blue,
And the earth is painted green,
With such a lot of nice fresh air
All sandwiched in between.

Unknown

Morning and Evening

Sounds of Morning

[1]Eleanor Farjeon

James Barton

Quickly

The tap-ping of sticks and the pat-ter of feet,

slowly ... *quickly*

The wind in the plane-trees that whis-per and rus-tle;

slowly ... *quickly*

The pi-geons all sleep-y, the news-boys all hus-tle,

very quickly

The *clip-pe-ty-clop* and the *clip-clop* a-gain,

Of sol-diers and hors-es, more hors-es than men.

[1]From *Over the Garden Wall* by Eleanor Farjeon. Copyright, 1933, by Eleanor Farjeon. Reprinted by permission.

The Morning Sun

Translated

Swedish Folk Song

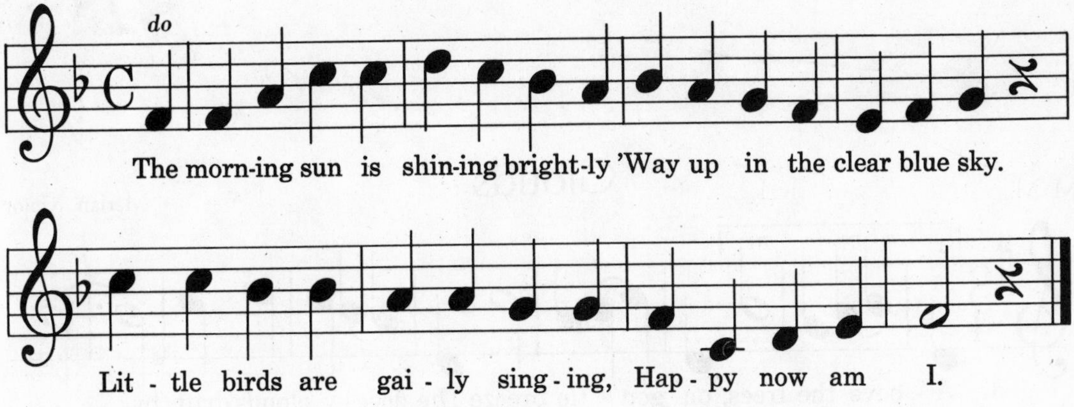

The morn-ing sun is shin-ing bright-ly 'Way up in the clear blue sky.

Lit - tle birds are gai - ly sing-ing, Hap - py now am I.

One Misty, Moisty Morning

Old Rhyme

Janice Edwards

One mist - y, moist - y morn - ing, When cloud - y was the weath - er,

I chanced to meet an old man Clothed all in leath - er.

He be - gan to com - pli-ment, And I be - gan to grin;

How do you do, and how do you do? And how do you do a - gain?

Clouds

M. M.

Marian Major

so mi re do mi

1. A - bove the trees, on gen - tle breeze The fleec - y clouds drift by.
2. The gold - en sun lights ev - 'ry one, They change as on they flow.

All down - y white, so sil - v'ry bright, They float a - cross the sky.
They're ev - er new a - gainst the blue; I won - der where they go?

Listen to "Waltz, Opus 91a," Schubert. (Victor Rhythm Album Four.)

Sky Pictures

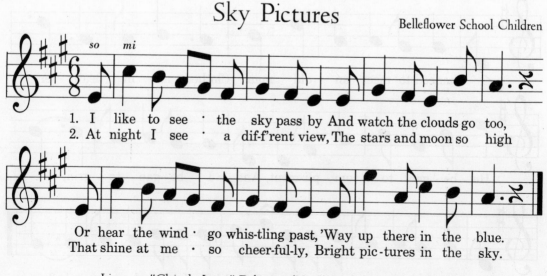

Belleflower School Children

so mi

1. I like to see · the sky pass by And watch the clouds go too,
2. At night I see · a dif-f'rent view, The stars and moon so high

Or hear the wind · go whis-tling past, 'Way up there in the blue.
That shine at me · so cheer-ful-ly, Bright pic-tures in the sky.

Listen to "Clair de Lune," Debussy. (Victor Listening Album Five.)

Star Light, Star Bright

Unknown

Children's Song

Star light, star bright, First star I've seen to-night.

I wish I may, I wish I might Have the wish I've wished to-night.

Evening in the Garden

Cecil Cowdrey

Jean Jacques Rousseau

do re do re mi re mi re do mi re

1. Eve - ning in the gar - den, Not a sound is heard
2. Si - lence in the gar - den, Si - lence on the hill;

Save when in the tree top Calls a sleep-y bird.
La - dy Nic - o - ti - na Wak - ens white and still.

Through the reeds and grass - es Wan - d'ring wa-ters drip;
Gone the chil-dren's voic - es, Fades the sun-set light,

At their cool-ing edg - es Thirst - y flow-ers sip.
Leave the gar-den dream - ing, Dream-ing in the night.

107

There's a starlit stair to the golden moon.—*Author Unknown*

Song at Dusk

Nancy Byrd Turner

Paul Forde

Drowsily

la la ti do re mi do la

1. The flow-ers nod, the shad-ows creep, A star comes o-ver the hill;
2. The world is full of drows-y things, And sweet with can - dle - light;

The young-est lamb has gone to sleep, The small-est bird is still.
The nests are full of fold-ed wings. Good night, good night, good night.

The Moon Ship

From the Japanese

so

In the o-cean of the sky, Borne on ris-ing waves of cloud, The

(○)

moon ship goes a - glid-ing by Through a for-est of stars.

This song is played on black keys only.

How many of you can play it on the piano, using both hands?

108

Wind, Rain and Weather

All the streets are a-shine with rain
The other side of my window pane.
Each motor car unrolls a track
Of red or green on the asphalt's black.
Beneath umbrellas people ply
Like giant toadstools stalking by.

Rachel Field

Up Goes My Umbrella

V. M. S.

Verna Meade Surer

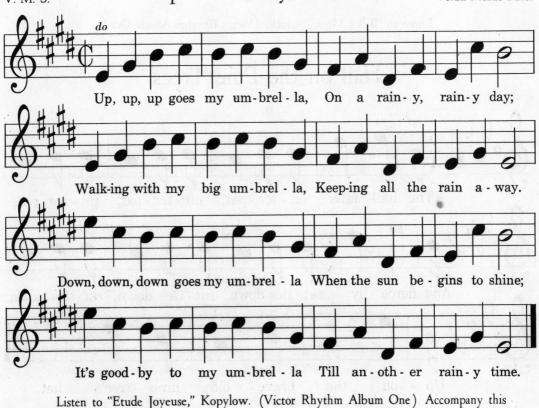

Up, up, up goes my um-brel-la, On a rain-y, rain-y day;

Walk-ing with my big um-brel-la, Keep-ing all the rain a-way.

Down, down, down goes my um-brel-la When the sun be-gins to shine;

It's good-by to my um-brel-la Till an-oth-er rain-y time.

Listen to "Etude Joyeuse," Kopylow. (Victor Rhythm Album One) Accompany this music with rain rattles or maracas.

Rain, Rain, Rain!

Abbie Farwell Brown

L. B. P.

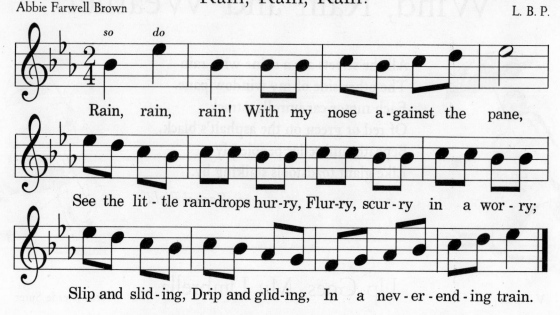

so   *do*

Rain, rain, rain! With my nose a-gainst the pane,

See the lit - tle rain-drops hur-ry, Flur-ry, scur-ry in a wor-ry;

Slip and slid-ing, Drip and glid-ing, In a nev-er-end-ing train.

Listen to "Ballet Music," Gluck. (Victor Rhythm Album One.)

Hail on the Pine Trees

From the Japanese

mi   *la*

The hail falls pit - ter - pat, pit - ter - pat, pit - ter - pat,

And fierce - ly rat - tles down, rat - tles down, rat - tles down,

Up - on the brave old pine tree's hat.

You can play all of this song on the black keys of the piano.

Pit-a-Pat[1]

Alice C. D. Riley

Jessie L. Gaynor

1. Pit - a - pat, pit - a - pat, Fall the ti - ny rain - drops,
2. Ev - 'ry leaf, ev - 'ry flow'r, Bids the rain-drops wel - come,

Plash - ing, oh so light - ly, on the win - dow pane.
While the thirst - y earth with glad - ness drinks her fill,

Pit - a - pat, pit - a - pat, Hear their voic - es call - ing,
Pit - a - pat, pit - a - pat, Wash - ing ev - 'ry pet - al,

'Tis a sum - mer show - er, 'Tis the fall - ing rain.
Fill - ing ev - 'ry brook and ev - 'ry ti - ny rill.

Pit - a - pat, pit - a - pat, drip, drip, drop,

Pit - a - pat, pit - a - pat, drip, drip, drop.

1From *Songs of the Child World*, by Jessie L. Gaynor, published and copyrighted, 1897, by the John Church Company. Used by permission.

Lightly Row

Traditional Song

Light-ly row, light-ly row, O'er the shin-ing waves we go;

Smooth-ly glide, smooth-ly glide On the si-lent tide;

Let the winds and wa-ters be Still and calm and clear to see;

Sing and float, sing and float In our lit-tle boat.

Listen to "In a Boat (*En Bateau*)," Debussy (Victor or Columbia record), and to "Boating on the Lake," Kullak. (Victor Rhythm Album Two.)

Sailing

Godfrey Marks

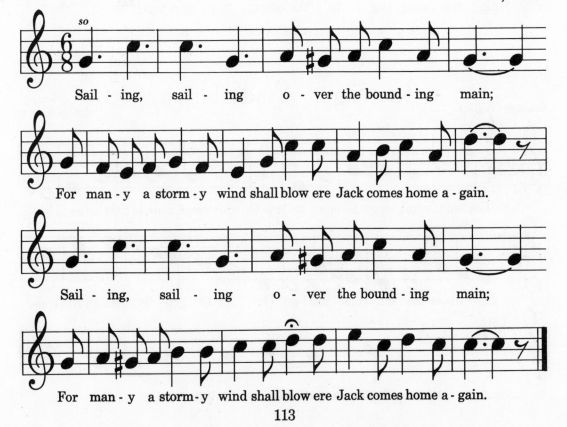

Sail - ing, sail - ing o - ver the bound - ing main;

For man - y a storm - y wind shall blow ere Jack comes home a - gain.

Sail - ing, sail - ing o - ver the bound - ing main;

For man - y a storm - y wind shall blow ere Jack comes home a - gain.

Wind in the Trees

L. B. P.

German Folk Tune

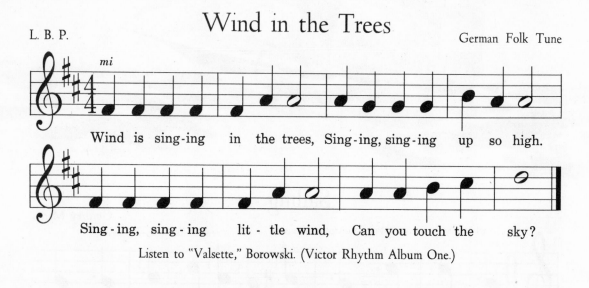

mi

Wind is sing-ing   in the trees, Sing-ing, sing-ing   up so high.

Sing-ing, sing-ing   lit-tle wind, Can you touch the   sky?

Listen to "Valsette," Borowski. (Victor Rhythm Album One.)

The Night Wind's Lullaby

Adelaide Walker

Helen S. Leavitt

mi

The night wind sings a song to me Of whis-pered sounds that seem to be

Lull-a-bies low that come and go, That sing so gen-tly through the trees

A   sleep - y   song   to   me.

Autumn

September's harvest days are done.
October's colored leaves have fun.
November's chilly winds do run.

September

Edward Bliss Reed

Sally Bowen

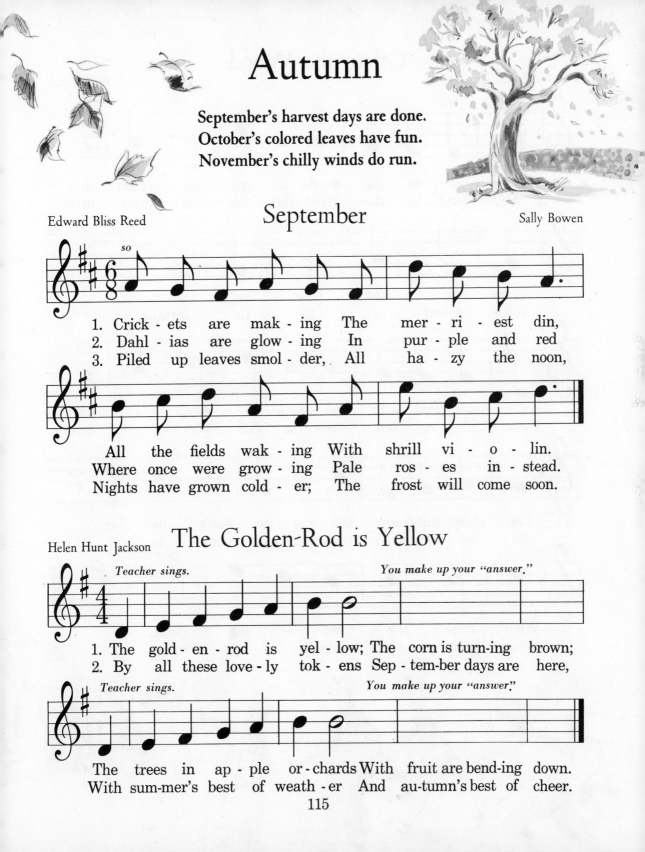

1. Crick-ets are mak-ing The mer-ri-est din,
2. Dahl-ias are glow-ing In pur-ple and red
3. Piled up leaves smol-der, All ha-zy the noon,

All the fields wak-ing With shrill vi-o-lin.
Where once were grow-ing Pale ros-es in-stead.
Nights have grown cold-er; The frost will come soon.

The Golden-Rod is Yellow

Helen Hunt Jackson

Teacher sings.

You make up your "answer."

1. The gold-en-rod is yel-low; The corn is turn-ing brown;
2. By all these love-ly tok-ens Sep-tem-ber days are here,

Teacher sings.

You make up your "answer."

The trees in ap-ple or-chards With fruit are bend-ing down.
With sum-mer's best of weath-er And au-tumn's best of cheer.

115

Off to the Woods

Christine Turner Curtis

Peter Dalton

1. We're off to the woods on an au - tumn day,
2. We'll hunt for the trees where the chest - nuts drop

When winds are blow - ing loud;
With pound of lit - tle drums,

With pails and with bas - kets a - way, a - way,
Then fill up our pails to the ver - y top,

The chest - nuts are fall - ing, so don't de - lay;
So we can have chest-nuts with corn to pop,

We'll race the rac - ing cloud.
When snow - y win - ter comes.

Bonfire

Christine Turner Curtis

Louise Giere

do

1. All down the vil - lage street the bon - fires blaze.
2. Scoop up the crack-ling leaves, and each in turn,
3. See how the danc-ing flames leap up and spring;

Now is the gold - en end of sum - mer days.
Toss them up - on the fire and watch them burn.
Join hands a - round the fire and dance and sing.

Autumn Leaves Falling

Marian Major

M. M.

mi

Au - tumn leaves fall - ing, win - ter is call - ing,

Flow - ers have gone to sleep.

Cold winds are blow - ing, soon it will be snow-ing;

faster

May - be it will be deep.

Winter

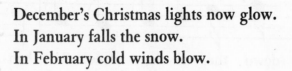

December's Christmas lights now glow.
In January falls the snow.
In February cold winds blow.

White Fields

James Stephens

Lydia Elwood

Trudging tempo

1. In the win-ter time we go Walk-ing in the fields of snow;
2. Point-ing out the way we came, -Ev - 'ry one of them the same-

Where there is no grass at all; Where the top of ev - 'ry wall,
All a-cross the fields there be Prints in sil - ver fil - i - gree;

Ev - 'ry fence, and ev - 'ry tree, Is as white as white can be.
And our moth - ers al-ways know,

By the foot-prints in the snow, Where it is the chil-dren go.

Snow

Paul Forde

Snow, snow, soft, white snow, Snow, snow, vel - vet snow,

Snow all day and snow all night, Snow, snow so soft and white,

Snow, snow, soft, white snow, Snow, snow, gen - tle snow,

Cov-er the earth with your blan-ket white, And soft-ly say, "Good night, good night."

January

Alice E. Allen

Velma Hanlin

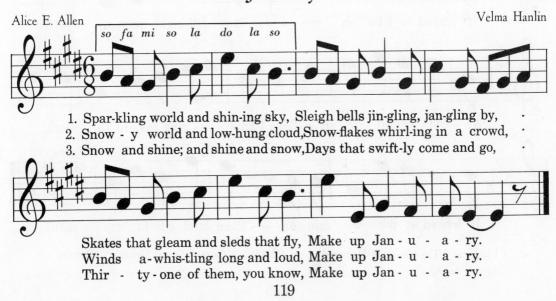

so fa mi so la do la so

1. Spar-kling world and shin-ing sky, Sleigh bells jin-gling, jan-gling by,
2. Snow - y world and low-hung cloud, Snow-flakes whirl-ing in a crowd,
3. Snow and shine; and shine and snow, Days that swift-ly come and go,

Skates that gleam and sleds that fly, Make up Jan - u - a - ry.
Winds a-whis-tling long and loud, Make up Jan - u - a - ry.
Thir - ty - one of them, you know, Make up Jan - u - a - ry.

Snowflakes

Isla P. Richardson

Velma Hanlin

I watched a snow-flake Come sail-ing from the sky, .

It played a joke on me when It fell right in my eye! .

An-oth-er lit-tle snow-flake Came dan-cing toward the south,

It looked at me a min-ute — Then land-ed in my mouth!

Listen to "The Snow is Dancing" from Children's Corner Suite, Debussy. (Victor or Columbia record.)

Ting! ring! the sleigh-bells jingle
  Merrily over the frozen snow.
Cheeks a-glow and ears a-tingle,
  Tumble in, children, here we go!

Ting! ring! the sleigh-bells jingle!
  Snow-wreaths fly like a snow-sea's foam.
Sweet bells, sweet laugh, hark! how they mingle!
  Tumble out, children, here we're at home!

Laura E. Richards

Sleigh Ride

James Barton

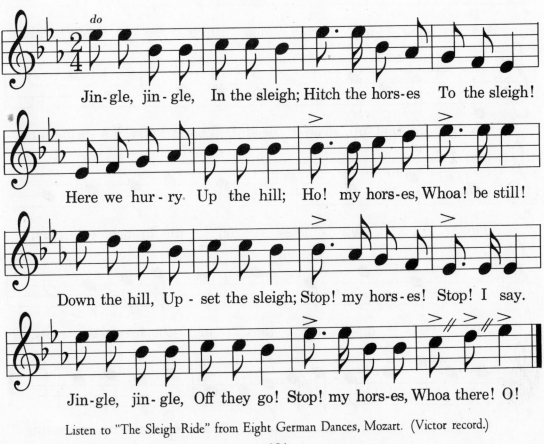

Jin-gle, jin-gle, In the sleigh; Hitch the hors-es To the sleigh!

Here we hur-ry Up the hill; Ho! my hors-es, Whoa! be still!

Down the hill, Up-set the sleigh; Stop! my hors-es! Stop! I say.

Jin-gle, jin-gle, Off they go! Stop! my hors-es, Whoa there! O!

Listen to "The Sleigh Ride" from Eight German Dances, Mozart. (Victor record.)

Spring

In March peep out the early flowers.
In April come the sunny showers.
In May birds sing in leafy bowers.

Springtime

V. M. S.

Verna Meade Surer

Wake up, wake up and hear the rob - ins sing,

They're sing - ing, bring - ing mes - sag - es of spring.

Oh, get up, get up, sleep - y - head. Don't you know it's spring-time?

Puss - y wil - lows on the branch - es play,

And buds on tree tops in the breez - es sway.

In the gar - den birds all seem to say, "Wake up, wake up, it's spring!"

A Bird Came

V. H.

Velma Hanlin

This morn-ing a bird came and sang this hap-py tune, ·

Chee - ree, · chee - ree, · chee - ree. · ·

He came to say that spring - time is com - ing soon. ·

Chee - ree, · chee - ree, · chee - ree. · ·

White Dove

Paraphrased by
Christine Turner Curtis

Puerto Rican

1. "Tell me, lit - tle dove, white and snow - y, Where your nest is swing-ing."
2. "Tell me, lit - tle dove, white and snow - y, Whith-er are you flit-ting?"
3. "Tell me why you light on a rose tree, Where the thorns are grow-ing."

"In the green, green heart of a pine tree, Near-by flow-ers spring-ing."
"To the green, green bough of a pine tree. There I shall be sit-ting."
"Here I hope to see in the spring-time Ros-es, red and glow-ing."

Cheerio!

J. G. G.

June Goethe Garrels

mi

"Cheer - i - o," the birds sing, "Cheer - i - o," all day.

Mer - ri - ly the cheer - y notes will waft our way.

It's the time for danc - ing, mel - o - dy and fun,

Come a - long then, sing your song then, ev - 'ry - one.

Listen to "The Birds," Respighi. (Victor records.)

Tra La La

Translated by Mary E. Holland

French

do

Do you hear the lit - tle · bird

Sing - ing on the big elm · tree?

Tra la la la la la la la la la la,

Tra la la, tra la la.

Pussy Willow

Traditional

I know a little pussy, Her coat is silver gray; She lives down in the meadow,

Not very far away. Although she is a pussy, She'll never be a cat,

For she's a pussy willow, Now what do you think of that?*

Meow, meow, meow, meow, meow, meow, meow, meow, *Scat!*

This song is begun with all players in a crouching position. Rise slowly with each measure, finally standing up at * Slowly return to crouch, arriving on the last "meow." At "Scat" jump up and clap hands high over head.

I know
Where the wind flowers blow!
I know,
I have been
Where the little rabbits run
In the warm, yellow sun!

Irene Rutherford McLeod[1]

In Father's Lovely Garden

Translated

French Folk Song

In fa-ther's love-ly gar-den, Come, see the ros-es!

In fa-ther's love-ly gar-den, Come, see the ros-es,

And there's an or-ange tree, or-ange tree, or-ange tree,

And there's an or-ange tree. Fa-ther says they bloom for me.

Listen to "Spring Song," Mendelssohn. (Victor Listening Album Three.)

[1] From *Songs to Save a Soul*, by Irene Rutherford McLeod. Reprinted by permission of Chatto and Windus.

Summer Breeze

Old Garden Rhyme

John Langland

Sum-mer breeze, so soft-ly blow-ing, In my gar - den pinks are grow-ing;

If you'll go · and send the show-ers, You may come and smell my flow-ers.

Cherries Are Ripe

As sung by Mrs. Barbara Goin

American Folk Song

Cher-ries are ripe, cher-ries are ripe And Bar-ba-ra shall have some.

Rob - in wants no cher - ry pie, Quick he eats and a - way he'll fly;

But my lit-tle child, so gen-tle and mild, She sure-ly shall have some pie.

Who Will Come With Me

Lady Bell

From "Singing Circle"

1, 2, 3, 4. Who will come with me, the jol-ly, jol-ly rov-er?

Who will come with me and roam the wide world o-ver,

And see, and see, and see what we can see?

All the fish that swim in the sea,   Swim-ming, swim-ming, swim-ming to me,
All the birds that hop in the tree,   Hop-ping, hop-ping, hop-ping to me,
Ev-'ry buzz-ing bum-ble-y bee,   Buzz-ing, buzz-ing, buzz-ing to me,
Ev-'ry rid-er o-ver the lea,   Rid-ing, rid-ing, rid-ing to me,

All the fish that swim in the sea,   Swim-ming up to me.
All the birds that hop in the tree,   Hop-ping up to me.
Ev-'ry buzz-ing bum-ble-y bee,   Buzz-ing up to me.
Ev-'ry rid-er o-ver the lea,   Rid-ing up to me.

Bugs and Other Things

And the fireflies in the bushes
Prick the darkness all around;
And the crickets, very busy,
Make their night-time summer sound.

Dorothy Aldis[1]

Lady Bug, Lady Bug!

Old Rhyme · Children's Song

La-dy Bug, La-dy Bug, fly a-way home, Fly a-way home, fly a-way home!

Your house is on fire and your chil-dren are gone, Chil-dren are gone, gone, gone, gone,

All but one and her name is Anne, Her name is Anne, her name is Anne,

She hid un-der the fry-ing pan, The fry-ing pan, the fry-ing pan.

[1] From *Before Things Happen*, by Dorothy Aldis. Copyright, 1939, by Dorothy Aldis. Courtesy of G. P. Putnam's Sons.

Fuzzy Caterpillar

P. K. F.

Pauline K. Fisher

A fuzz-y cat-er-pil-lar went out for a walk, His
back went up and down. He crawled and he crawled and he
crawled and he crawled Till he crawled all o-ver town. He
was-n't dis-ap-point-ed, not a bit, to be a worm, Not a
tear was in his eye; For you see, he knew that some
day he'd be A ver-y love-ly but-ter-fly.

Listen to "Moths and Butterflies," Elgar. (Victor Listening Album Two.)

Butterfly

Teacher sings.   *You make up your "answer."*

But - ter -fly,   but - ter - fly,   flut-ter, flut-ter,   flut-ter high,

But-ter-fly,   but-ter-fly,   flut-ter, flut-ter   to the sky.

White Butterflies

Algernon Charles Swinburne   Louise Giere

do

Fly, white but-ter-flies, out to sea, Frail, pale wings for the wind to try,

Small white wings that we scarce can see,   Fly!   Fly!

ritard

Some fly light as a laugh of glee, Some fly soft as a long, low sigh;

All to the hav-en where each would be,   Fly!   Fly!   Fly!

Listen to "The Butterfly," Grieg. (Victor record.)

The Woodpecker

Elizabeth Madox Roberts [1]

Ray Green

The wood-peck-er pecked out a lit-tle round hole,

And made him a house in the tel-e-phone-pole.

One day when I watched he poked out his head,

And he had on a hood and a col-lar of red.

When the streams of rain pour out of the sky,

And the spar-kles of light-ning go flash-ing by,

[1]From *Under the Tree*, by Elizabeth Madox Roberts. Copyright 1922 by B. W. Huebsch, Inc. Reprinted by permission of The Viking Press, Inc., New York.

And the big, big wheels of the thun - der roll,

He can snug - gle back in the tel - e - phone - pole.

Buzz, Buzz, Buzz

Translated from the German by
Frederic Field Bullard

Carl Reinecke

so

1. Buzz, buzz, buzz; bus - y, buzz - y bee!
2. Buzz, buzz, buzz; bus - y, buzz - y bee!

so ti re fa mi ti do la

Take from ev - 'ry pret - ty flow - er Drops of hon - ey to your bow - er.
Won't you please give me some hon - ey On this morn - ing bright and sun - ny?

Buzz, buzz, buzz; bus - y, buzz - y bee!
Buzz, buzz, buzz; bus - y, buzz - y bee!

Listen to "The Bee," Schubert. (Victor Listening Album Three.)

Who's In?

Elizabeth Fleming

Louella Garrett

"The door is shut fast And ev - 'ry - one's out."

But peo - ple don't know What they're talk - ing a - bout!

Says the fly on the wall, And the flame on the coals,

And the dog on his rug, And the mice in their holes,

And the kit - ten curled up, And the spid - ers that spin --

"What! ev - 'ry - one out? Why! ev - 'ry - one's in!"

There Sat a Little Ant

French Fable translated

Jacques Armin

There sat a lit-tle ant on the horn of an ox,

Home from the fields slow-ly plod-ding.

"From where have you come?" said a cun-ning lit-tle fox.

The ant then re-plied, smart-ly nod-ding,

"Where have I come from? Sure-ly you can see.

Why, we've been out plow-ing, the ox and me!"

On the Farm

Old MacDonald Had a Farm

Traditional

1. Old Mac-Don-ald had a farm, E - I - E - I - O!
2. Old Mac-Don-ald had a farm, E - I - E - I - O!

And on this farm he had some chicks, E - I - E - I - O!
And on this farm he had some ducks, E - I - E - I - O!

With a chick, chick here, and a chick, chick there,
With a quack, quack here, and a quack, quack there,

Here a chick, there a chick, ev - 'ry - where a chick, chick.
Here a quack, there a quack, ev - 'ry - where a quack, quack.

Old Mac-Don-ald had a farm, E - I - E - I - O!
Old Mac-Don-ald had a farm, E - I - E - I - O!

Additional stanzas may be sung about a turkey, a pig, and all the other farm animals you know. With each new stanza it is fun to repeat the farmyard sounds in the earlier stanzas, just before you sing the last line of the song.

My Rooster

Paraphrased by
Christine Turner Curtis

Costa Rican

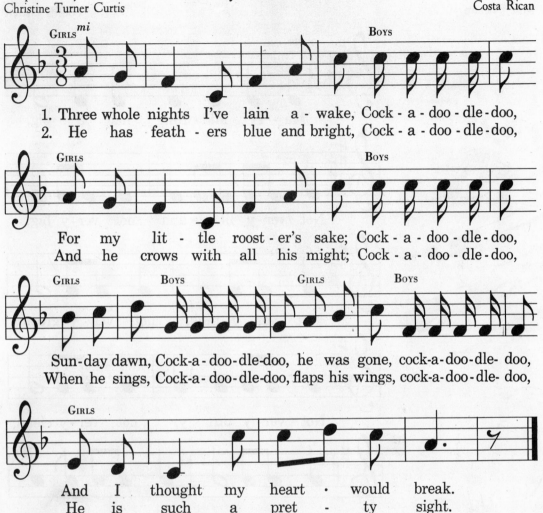

1. Three whole nights I've lain a-wake, Cock-a-doo-dle-doo,
2. He has feath-ers blue and bright, Cock-a-doo-dle-doo,

For my lit-tle roost-er's sake; Cock-a-doo-dle-doo,
And he crows with all his might; Cock-a-doo-dle-doo,

Sun-day dawn, Cock-a-doo-dle-doo, he was gone, cock-a-doo-dle-doo,
When he sings, Cock-a-doo-dle-doo, flaps his wings, cock-a-doo-dle-doo,

And I thought my heart would break.
He is such a pret-ty sight.

3. France and Spain I've hunted through, Cock-a-doodle-doo,
   Then to Germany I flew; Cock-a-doodle-doo,
   No bird there, Cock-a-doodle-doo, anywhere, cock-a-doodle-doo,
   Not in England or Peru.

4. So, kind friends, both far and near, Cock-a-doodle-doo,
   To my pleading now give ear; Cock-a-doodle-doo,
   Find my pet, Cock-a-doodle-doo, don't forget, cock-a-doodle-doo,
   Bring me back my rooster dear!

Listen to "Hens and Roosters" from the Carnival of Animals, Saint-Saëns. (Victor record.)

Mary Middling

Rose Fyleman   Louella Garrett

do

Ma - ry Mid - dling had a pig,

Not ver - y lit - tle and not ver - y big,

Not ver - y pink, not ver - y green,

Not ver - y dirt - y, not ver - y clean,

Not ver - y good, not ver - y naugh - ty,

Not ver - y hum - ble, not ver - y haugh - ty,

Not ver - y thin, not ver - y fat; Now

what would you give for a pig like that?

Who's That Ringing

Anonymous

Paul Forde

do

"Who's that ring-ing at my front door bell?" Meow, meow, meow.

"I'm a lit-tle black cat and I'm not ver-y well, Meow, meow, meow."

"Then put your nose in this bowl of mut-ton fat,

For that's the way to cure a puss-y cat;

snap fingers

So come right in and I'll fix you quick as that." Meow, meow, meow-rrrr.

A Farmer Went to Market

Paul Edmonds   James Seton

1. A farm-er went to mar-ket to buy a lit-tle pig, A
farm-er bought a big pig, a *ver-y big* · pig, Though

lit-tle pig, a pig-gy-wig, a ver--y lit-tle pig. Oh,
not at all a lit-tle pig, but real-ly rath-er big. He

all the pigs were big pigs, much too big, But the

farm-er did-n't care a fig, He *had* to buy a pig. 2. So the

was so ver-y proud of it he had to dance a jig, He

danced a-bout, He pranced a-bout 'Til off came his wig, But the

farm-er did-n't care a fig, He *had* to have a pig.

Woodchuck Hill

Frances Frost

Lydia Elwood

so *do* *mi* *re*

1. I saw a ba-by wood-chuck Sit-ting on a knoll,
2. His lit-tle broth-er squeaked And bumped and bowled him o-ver!

so *la*

Blink-ing in the sun-light, Fat and brown and droll.
They fought like in-fant fu-ries For a bunch of clo-ver!

He ate a head of clo-ver, And then he ate an-oth-er,
Then spanked were they in sun-shine · By their firm-pawed moth-er,

But when he grabbed a big paw-ful, Up popped his lit-tle broth-er!
Who marched them up the hill to home, The wood-chuck and his broth-er!

Nibblety, Nibblety, Nib

Anonymous

Marian Deere

First group

Three lit - tle rab - bits were eat - ing their lunch.

Second group

Nib - ble - ty, nib - ble - ty, nib - ble - ty, nib - ble - ty, nib, nib, nib.

With their heads to - geth - er, oh, how they did munch.

Nib - ble - ty, nib - ble - ty, nib - ble - ty, nib - ble - ty, nib, nib, nib.

They nib - bled so hard and they all were so quick.

Nib - ble - ty, nib - ble - ty, nib - ble - ty, nib - ble - ty, nib, nib, nib.

They fin-ished it up be-fore you could say "Tick."

Nib-ble-ty, nib-ble-ty, nib-ble-ty, nib-ble-ty, nib, nib, nib.

Wonderful Weather For Ducks

J. G. G.

June Goethe Garrels

1. It's won-der-ful weath-er for ducks, they say, Rain, rain, rain.
2. So out in the gar-den they splash their way, Rain, rain, rain.

O - pen the win-dows and let them play, Rain, rain, rain.
Sun-shine may come on an - oth - er day, Rain, rain, rain.

Lit - tle ducks so yel-low and sweet, Wear-ing rub - bers on their feet,
Bead - y eyes so ti - ny and brown, Feath-ers like a gold - en crown,

Wig-gling and wad-dling and quack-ing a - way, Rain, rain, rain.
Splash-ing and pad-dling, I hope they won't drown, Rain, rain, rain.

Hop! O'er the Fields

Translated by Alma A. Turechek

Czech Folk Song

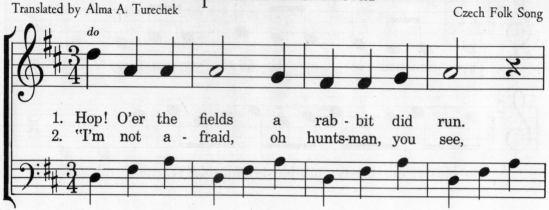

1. Hop! O'er the fields   a rab - bit did   run.
2. "I'm not a - fraid,   oh hunts-man, you   see,

Out   of   the   wheat   a   hunts-man   did   come.
I'll   run   and   hide   be - hind   a   big   tree.

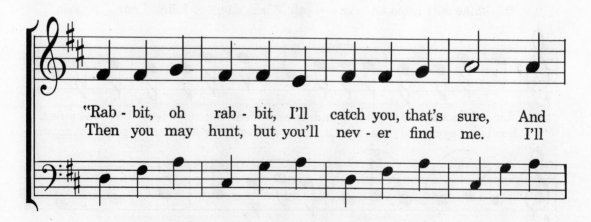

"Rab - bit,   oh   rab - bit,   I'll   catch   you, that's   sure,   And
Then   you   may   hunt, but   you'll   nev - er   find   me.   I'll

How many of you can play this song on the piano with both hands?

make ti - ny mit - tens from your snow - y fur."
watch you go by, and then hop off with glee."

Listen to "Of Br'er Rabbit," MacDowell. (Victor Listening Album Three.)

Ringaling, Tingaling Home

Nancy Byrd Turner

Ethel Anthony

1. Down in the coun - try when the dew is fall - ing,
2. Red - dy and Crum - pet, But - ter - cup and Clo - ver,

Back to their sup - per the good cows come.
Dai - sy and Cher - ry and Cream - pot come.

"Co, boss! Co, boss!" some - bod - y's call - ing.
"Co, boss! Co, boss!" some - bod - y's call - ing.

Ting - a - ling, ring - a - ling, ting - a - ling home.
Ting - a - ling, ring - a - ling, ting - a - ling home.

Tadpoles

Rose Fyleman

Paul Forde

1. Ten little tad-poles play-ing in a pool,
2. Ten lit-tle tad-poles swim-ming in and out,

"Come," said the wa-ter-rat, "come a-long to school.
Rac-ing and div-ing and turn-ing round a-bout.

Come and say your ta-bles, sit-ting in a row."
"Come now," said their moth-er, "din-ner time, I guess."

And all the lit-tle tad-poles said, "No no, no."
And all the lit-tle tad-poles said, "Yes, yes, yes."

Three Blind Mice

Traditional

Three blind mice, three blind mice, See how they run,

See how they run! They all ran aft-er the farm-er's wife, She

146

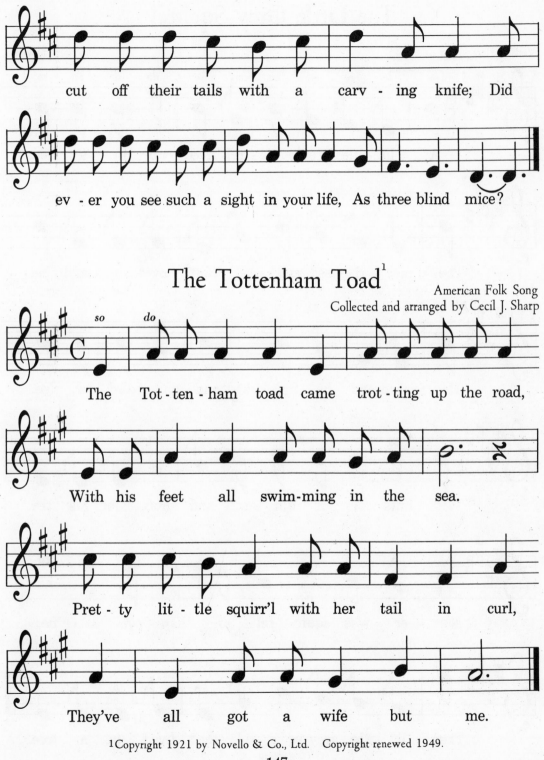

cut off their tails with a carv-ing knife; Did ev-er you see such a sight in your life, As three blind mice?

The Tottenham Toad[1]

American Folk Song
Collected and arranged by Cecil J. Sharp

so do

The Tot-ten-ham toad came trot-ting up the road,

With his feet all swim-ming in the sea.

Pret-ty lit-tle squirr'l with her tail in curl,

They've all got a wife but me.

The Little Grey Squirrel

Vernon Hart

Walter Howland

A lit-tle grey squir-rel lived up in a tree,

The mer-ri-est squir-rel that ev-er could be.

He frisked and he frol-icked and gam-boled for glee,

With nuts for his din-ner and nuts for his tea.

Nev-er was squir-rel so hap-py as he,

That lit-tle grey squir-rel that lived in a tree.

Ride My Horse, Giddap

Translated

Italian Children's Song

mi *do*

1. Ride my horse, gid - dap, gid-dap, Eat the oats I give to you.
2. San Fran-ces-co's far a-way, We must get there sure to-day;

Wear the shoes I put on you To go to San Fran - ces - co.
Moth - er's wait - ing for her pets, To feed us tast - y ome - lets.

so *do*

Gid - dap, gid-dap, gid-dap, gid-dap, Gid - dap, gid-dap, gid - dap, gid-dap,

To San Fran, San Fran - ces - co.

Listen to first movement "Children playing in the park" from *The Pines of Rome*, Respighi. (Victor Record.)

Snow-White Little Burro

Paraphrased by
Christine Turner Curtis

Chilean

1. Snow-white lit - tle   bur - ro,   Car - ry me a - way
2. You have noth-ing,   noth - ing,   Neith- er chick nor hen.
3. One sheep will sup - port   me,   One will give me milk;

To   my home in   child - hood,   Where I   used to   play.
Three white sheep I'm   tend - ing   In a   lit - tle   pen.
One   will   give me   wool - en,   Warm - er   far than   silk.

Listen to "The Little White Donkey," Ibert. (Decca Album "Animal Pictures in Music.")

The Shepherd tends his sheep
To keep them safe from harm.
He keeps them from the cliffs so steep
So they'll not cause alarm.

When a little lamb is lost,
The Shepherd takes his crook in hand
And searches o'er the pasture land
For his little woolly lamb.

Cedarhurst School Children

Out Among the Fir Trees

Translated by Alma A. Turechek

Czech Folk Song

Out a-mong the fir trees, Bal-sam, pine and spruce trees,

Wool-ly sheep are graz-ing While the shep-herds watch at ease.

How many of you can play this song on the piano, using both hands?

Listen to "The Little Shepherd" from *Children's Corner Suite*, Debussy. (Victor Listening Album Two.)

The Shepherdess

Translated by
Susanna Myers

French Folk Song

so do re mi re do so

1. There was a lit-tle French girl, Oh, ron, ron, ron, pe-tit pa-ta-pon,
2. A cheese she made one morn-ing, Oh, ron, ron, ron, pe-tit pa-ta-pon,
3. Her cat was sly-ly watch-ing, Oh, ron, ron, ron, pe-tit pa-ta-pon,

There was a lit-tle French girl, A shep-herd-ess was she, ron, ron,
A cheese she made one morn-ing, A cream-y cheese made she, ron, ron,
Her cat was sly-ly watch-ing, A naugh-ty cat was he, ron, ron,

A shep-herd-ess was she.
A cream-y cheese made she.
A naugh-ty cat was he.

4. Now, Puss, don't put your paw in,
   Oh, ron, ron, ron, petit patapon,
   If once you put your paw in,
   I'll spank you pretty quick, ron, ron,
   I'll spank you pretty quick.

5. Puss did not put his paw in,
   Oh, ron, ron, ron, petit patapon,
   Puss didn't put his paw in,
   Instead his little tongue, ron, ron,
   Instead his little tongue.

6. So, round and round she chased him,
   Oh, ron, ron, ron, petit patapon,
   So, round and round she chased him,
   And round and round went he, ron, ron,
   And round and round went he.

ABOUT SINGING THINGS

I listen to the whistles
From my window on the street.
I listen to the whistles
When it's hard to go to sleep.

I hear the little tugboats
And the ocean liners too.
The little tugs say chug-a-chug,
And the ocean liners, whoo-oo-oo.

Low whistles—boo-oo-oom, boo-oo.
Shrill whistles—tree-e-e-e-t.
I listen to the whistles
From my window on the street.

Elizabeth Manson Scott and *Elizabeth Chidsay*[1]

[1]Taken from *Another Here and Now Story Book*, edited by Lucy Sprague Mitchell, published and copyright 1937 by E. P. Dutton & Co., Inc., New York.

Clocks and Bells

Hickory, Dickory, Dock!

Mother Goose

J. W. Elliott

Hick-o-ry, dick-o-ry, dock! The mouse ran up the clock.

Glissando up on the xylophone or piano.

The clock struck one, the mouse ran down. Hick-o-ry, dick-o-ry, dock.

Glissando down on the xylophone or piano.

Trippele, Trappele, Trop!

Karel de Gheldere

Remi Ghesquiere

Hick-o-ry, dick-o-ry, dock! The mouse ran up the clock.
Trip-pe-le, trap-pe-le, trop! De muis klom op de klok.

The clock struck one, The mouse ran down.
De klok-ke sloeg éen, De muis kwam be-neen;

This is the way the children in
Holland sing "Hickory, Dickory, Dock!"

Hick-o-ry, dick-o-ry, dock!
Trip-pe-le, trap-pe-le, trop!

Cuckoo Clock

G. H.

Graham Haswell

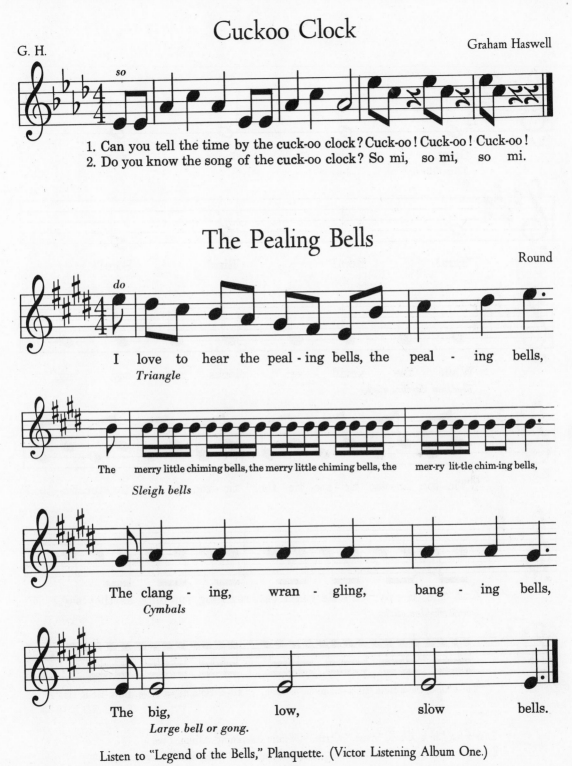

1. Can you tell the time by the cuck-oo clock? Cuck-oo! Cuck-oo! Cuck-oo!
2. Do you know the song of the cuck-oo clock? So mi,   so mi,   so mi.

The Pealing Bells

Round

I love to hear the peal - ing bells, the   peal - ing   bells,

Triangle

The   merry little chiming bells, the merry little chiming bells, the   mer-ry lit-tle chim-ing bells,

Sleigh bells

The clang - ing,   wran - gling,   bang - ing   bells,

Cymbals

The big,   low,   slow   bells.

Large bell or gong.

Listen to "Legend of the Bells," Planquette. (Victor Listening Album One.)

Clocks

Great big clocks say,

Tone block.

"Bim! Bom! Bim! Bom!"

While the small - er clocks are say - ing,

Medium rhythm sticks

"Tic - toc, tic - toc, tic - toc, tic - toc, tic - toc, tic - toc, tic - toc, tic - toc."

And the ti - ny lit - tle watch-es run-ning, run-ning as they say,

Small rhythm sticks

"Tic-a-tic-a, tic-a-tic-a, tic-a-tic-a, tic-a-tic-a, tic-a-tic-a, tic-a-tic-a, tic-a-tic-a, tic."

Listen to "In a Clock Store," Orth. (Victor Listening Album Five.)
Listen to second movement of the "Clock Symphony," Haydn. (Victor record.)

Big Bells Ringing

Teacher sings. *You make up your "answer."*

Big bells ring-ing, Bim! Bom! Bim! Bom!

Teacher sings. *You make up your "answer."*

Oth-er bells are ring-ing, ring-ing, Ding-ding, ding-ding, ding-ding, dong!

Merry Are the Bells

Mother Goose   June Golden

do

1. Mer-ry are the bells, and mer-ry would they ring,
2. Mer-ry have we met, and mer-ry have we been;

Mer-ry was my-self, and mer-ry could I sing;
Mer-ry let us part, and mer-ry meet a-gain;

With a mer-ry ding-dong, hap-py, gay and free,
With our mer-ry sing-song, hap-py, gay and free,

And a mer-ry sing-song, hap-py let us be!
And a mer-ry ding-dong, hap-py let us be!

Play triangles and bells while you sing this song.

Trains and Planes and Other Things

Big yellow trolley lumbers along,
Long black subway sings an undersong,
Airplanes swoop and flash in the sky,
Noisy old elevated goes rocketing by.

Tall fat buses on the Avenue,
They will stop for anyone—even—just—you.
All kinds of autos rush down the street.
And then there are always—your own two feet.

Leslie Thompson[1]

Trucks

James S. Tippett

Francis Hilliard

Heavily and slowly

Big trucks for steel beams, Big trucks for coal,

Rum-bling down the broad streets, Heav-i-ly they roll.

lightly and quickly

Lit-tle trucks for gro-cer-ies, Lit-tle trucks for bread,

Turn-ing in-to ev-'ry street, Rush-ing on a-head.

[1]Taken from *Another Here and Now Story Book*, edited by Lucy Sprague Mitchell, published and copyright 1937 by E. P. Dutton & Co., Inc., New York.

158

I Love to Hear the Train

Wymond Garthwaite   Charles J. Cromwell

I love to hear the train go by With a rum-ble that tick-les my

heels. The choof-e-ty-choof of the chim-ney stack And the

click-e-ty-click of the wheels, The choof-e-ty-choof of the

chim-ney stack And the click-e-ty-click of the wheels.

What is it coming so fast, so fast,
Growing bigger and bigger as nearer it comes?
What is it coming so loud, so loud,
Louder and louder as nearer it comes?
What makes the singing sound on the rails,
The long steel rails that shine in the sun?
What is this monster rushing past,
Ever so long and loud?

Roberta M. Whitehead

Train

Choof,   choof,   choof,   choof,

Chooooooo!   Whishhhhhhh! *(Make sound like escaping steam.)*

Little Red Caboose

Camp Song

Lit - tle red ca - boose, lit - tle red ca - boose,

Lit - tle red ca - boose be - hind the train, the train.

Smoke - stack on his back, go - ing down the track.

Lit - tle red ca-boose be-hind the train.   train. (Too - too - too!)

The Aeroplane

Rowena Bastin Bennett

Marian Major

No ea-gle flies through sun and rain So swift-ly as an aer-o-plane.

I wish she would come swoop-ing down Be-tween the stee-ples of the town

And swoop me right up off my feet And take me high a-bove the street,

That all the oth-er boys might see The lit-tle speck that would be me.

We Play and Sing

Bang, twang, clatter and clang,
Strum, thrum, upon fiddle and drum.

Charles Stuart Calverley

Johnny Schmoker

Traditional

do

John-ny Schmo-ker, John-ny Schmo-ker,

Can you sing, · can you play? ·

I can play up-on my fife. ·
I can play up-on my drum. ·
I can play up-on my vi-ol.

Twee-dle dee-dle dee, so sings my fife. ·
Rub-a-dub-a-dub, so sings my drum. ·
Zoom-a-zoom-a-zoom, so sings my vi-ol.

4. Flute   - Too-tle too-tle toot, so sings my flute.
5. Trombone - Taa-ta-ta-ta-taa, so sings my trombone.
6. Bagpipe - Wang-a-wang-a-wang, so sings my bagpipe.

After each stanza repeat the sounds of the instruments you sang in the earlier stanzas. It is fun to pretend to play each instrument as you sing. What instruments would you like to add to this song?

163

Marching Song

Laura E. Richards

Danish Folk Tune

1. If I were a drum-mer, if I were a drum-mer,
2. If I were a fid-dler, if I were a fid-dler,

How I would play with my drum-sticks two!
How I would han-dle my fid-dle bow!

Rub - a - dub - a - dub, dub; rub - a - dub - a - dub, dub!
Twee-dle, dee - dle, dee - dle; twee-dle, dee - dle, dee - dle!

Keep - ing the time and the meas - ure true.
Mer - ri - ly, cheer - i - ly, high and low.

Head up, eyes front, straight and pat,
Head up, eyes front, straight and pat,

Rub - a - dub, rub - a - dub, just like that.
Twee - dle, dee, twee - dle, dee, just like that.

Let's Play Band

Richard C. Berg

1. Ste-phen plays a trum - pet, Ste-phen plays a trum - pet,
2. Ma - ry plays a snare drum, Ma - ry plays a snare drum,
3. E - ric plays a bass drum, E - ric plays a bass drum,
4. Di - nah plays the cym - bals, Di - nah plays the cym - bals,

Ta, ta, ta, ta, ta, ta. Ste-phen plays a trum - pet,
Trum, ta, ta, tum, tum, trr--um. Ma - ry plays a snare drum,
Boom, bah, bah, boom, boom, boom. E - ric plays a bass drum,
Bing, bing a - bang, bong, crash! Di - nah plays the cym - bals,

Ste-phen plays a trum - pet, Ta, ta, ta, ta, ta, ta.
Ma - ry plays a snare drum, Trum, ta, ta, tum, tum, trr--um.
E - ric plays a bass drum, Boom, bah, bah, boom, boom, boom.
Di - nah plays the cym - bals, Bing, bing - a, bang, bong, crash!

What a Happy Day

German Folk Tune

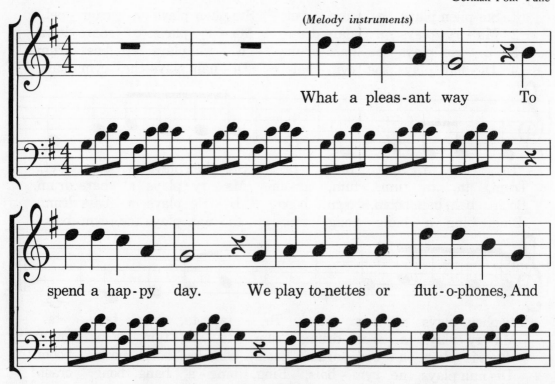

(Melody instruments)

What a pleas-ant way   To

spend a hap-py   day.   We play to-nettes or   flut-o-phones, And

oc - a - ri - nas, xy - lo - phones. What a hap - py day.

Who can play this piece on the piano while others sing the words or play the tune with melody instruments?

Theme

Ludwig van Beethoven, Op. 61

How many of you can play this piece on the piano?

First-Chair Player

Richard C. Berg

1. Fin-gers and tongue must both a - gree; Read ev - 'ry note: "F,   E,   G,   D."
2. Mu - sic must al - ways be in tune, Wheth - er on flute or big bas-soon.

Play ev-'ry meas-ure rhyth - mi - c'lly to be a first-chair play - er.
Don't o - ver-blow, and some-day soon you'll be a first-chair play - er.

Henry Berg

Playing the Flute and Drum

Portuguese Folk Tune

1. Too, too, too I play up - on my brand new flute;
2. Tum, tum, tum I play up - on my brand new drum;

When I play my tongue helps me to too, too, toot.
When I play the sticks go up and down, tum, tum.

Ev - 'ry time I press an - oth - er fin - ger down,
Bounc-ing drum-sticks up and down with good con - trol

Then the tune will change and make an - oth - er sound.
Helps us learn to play a long and stead - y roll.

168

SHINING HOURS

Eloise Wilkin

The Raggletaggletown Singers

By Frank Luther

This is the story of Bonkey Donkey,

Hee   haw!   Hee   haw!

Old Tog Dog,

Bow wow wow!   Bow wow wow!

The Old Fat Cat,

Me - ow! ·   Me - ow! ·

And the Old Red Rooster,

Cock - a - doo - dle - doo!   Cock - a - doo - dle - doo!

The Raggletaggletown Singers!

One day Bonkey Donkey went down the road crying,

"My mas-ter's driv-en me a-way from home, A-way from home,

a-way from home; My mas-ter's driv-en me a-way from home,

He says I'm too old to work. Hee haw! Hee haw!

He says I'm too old to work."

Bonkey Donkey went down the road 'til he came to Tog Dog, who sat by the side of the road crying,

"Bow wow wow! Bow wow wow!"

Bonkey Donkey said, "What's the matter, Tog Dog?" Tog Dog said,

"My mas-ter's driv-en me a - way from home, A - way from home,

a - way from home; My mas-ter's driv-en me a - way from home,

He says I'm too old to watch like a watch dog. Bow wow wow!

Bow wow wow! He says I'm too old to watch like a watch dog."

Bonkey Donkey said, "Well, Tog Dog, your voice is almost as good as mine. Come with me to Raggletaggletown and we'll be singers."

172

So they went down the road 'til they came to the Old
Fat Cat, who sat by the side of the road crying,

"Me - ow! · Me - ow!" ·

Bonkey Donkey said, "What's the matter, Fat Cat?"
Fat Cat said,

"My mas-ter's driv-en me a - way from home, A - way from home,

a - way from home; My mas-ter's driv-en me a - way from home,

He says I'm too old to catch mice. Me - ow! · Me - ow! ·

He   says   I'm   too   old   to   catch   mice."

Bonkey Donkey said, "Well, Fat Cat, your voice is almost as good as
Tog Dog's and mine. Come with us to Raggletaggletown and we'll be
singers."

So they went down the road 'til they came to the Old Red
Rooster, who sat by the side of the road crying,

"Cock - a - doo - dle - doo!   Cock - a - doo - dle-doo!"

Bonkey Donkey said, "What's the matter, Old Red Rooster?" The Old
Rooster said,

"My mas-ter's going to make me in - to stew,   Me   in - to   stew,

me in - to   stew;   My mas-ter's going to make me in - to   stew,

He   says I'm too old   to   crow   in   the morn - ing.

Cock - a - doo - dle - doo!   Cock - a - doo - dle - doo!

He   says I'm too old   to   crow   in   the morn - ing."

174

Bonkey Donkey said, "Well, Old Rooster, your voice is almost as good as Tog Dog's and Fat Cat's and mine. Come with us to Raggletaggletown and we'll be singers." So they went down the road 'til they came to a deep wood. Soon it was night and they were sleepy.

So the don-key went to sleep un-der-neath the tree,

The dog went to sleep at the bot-tom of the tree,

The cat went to sleep on a limb of the tree,

And the roost-er flew up in the top of the tree.

Penny Dance and Well, Old Dobbey, you must
Dog Does and I. Said and nine. Come with us
and we'll be Master. So they went down the road. So they came to

Soon the rooster called down, "Cock-a-doodle-doo! I see a light through the trees. Maybe there's a house where we can get some supper."

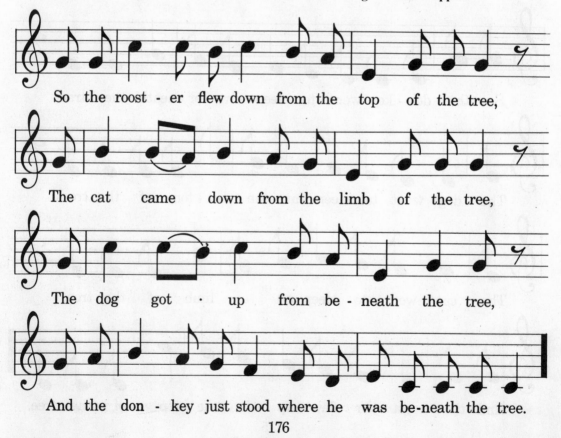

So the roost - er flew down from the top of the tree,

The cat came down from the limb of the tree,

The dog got up from be - neath the tree,

And the don - key just stood where he was be-neath the tree.

Well, they went through the wood 'til they came to a little house with a light shining through the window. The donkey put his feet up on the window sill; the dog jumped up on the donkey's back; the cat jumped up on the dog's back; and the rooster flew 'way up on the cat's back; and they all looked in the window; and what do you think they saw?

They saw a band of robbers sitting around a table covered with food. The donkey said, "Now maybe if we sing a sweet song they'll ask us in to supper."

So the donkey sang,

The old dog sang,

"Hee haw!   Hee haw!"

"Bow wow wow!   Bow wow wow!"

The fat cat sang,

The rooster sang,

"Me-ow!   Me-ow!"

"Cock-a-doo-dle-doo!   Cock-a-doo-dle-doo!"

Then they all sang together,

"Hee   haw!   Hee   haw!   Hee

"Bow   wow   wow!   Bow   wow   wow!

"Me - ow!   .   Me - ow!   .   Me -

"Cock - a - doo - dle-doo!   Cock - a - doo - dle-doo!

haw!   Hee   haw!"

Bow   wow   wow!   Bow   wow   wow!"

ow!   .   Me - ow!"   .

Cock - a - doo - dle-doo!   Cock - a - doo - dle-doo!"

When the robbers heard the terrible noise they were so frightened they ran away. So the donkey, the dog, the cat and the rooster went into the little house. They sat down at the table and began to eat.

1. Ap - ple sauce and chopped chick - en liv - er steak,
2. Or - ang -es, ba - na - nas and tur - key legs,

Rab - bit stew and lamb stew and an - gel cake,
Can - dy mints and choc -'lates and hard - boiled eggs.

Lim - a beans and string beans and rare roast beef
They are ver - y hap - py and ver - y good,

And sweet po - ta - to pie on a let - tuce leaf.
There in the lit - tle house in the green, green wood.

Well, they never did get to Raggletaggletown, but they didn't care. Even to this day they live happily in the little house in the wood and every night after the dishes are put away they sing their sweet song.

The donkey,
"Hee haw! Hee haw!"

Old dog,
"Bow wow wow! Bow wow wow!"

Fat cat,
"Me-ow! Me-ow!"

The rooster,
"Cock-a-doo-dle-doo! Cock-a-doo-dle-doo!"

"Hee haw!   Hee haw!   Hee haw! Hee haw! Hee

"Bow wow wow!   Bow wow wow!   Bow wow wow!

"Me - ow!   .   Me - ow!   .   Me - ow!   .   Me -

"Cock-a-doo-dle-doo!   Cock-a-doo-dle-doo!   Cock-a-doo-dle-doo!

haw! Hee haw!"

Bow   wow   wow!"

ow!   .   Me - ow!"

Cock - a - doo - dle-doo!"

The Ugly Duckling

By Frank Luther

This is the story of the Ugly Duckling.

Down in the mead-ow is a pond

Where the hens cluck-cluck and the ducks quack-quack.

Down in the mead-ow is a pond And a-round the pond is a bank,

And on the bank is a nest, And in the nest are the eggs,

And on the eggs sits Moth-er Duck; Down in the mead-ow by the pond.

There are six eggs in the nest, five duck eggs and one big egg, and every
day Mother Duck would count them, as Mother Ducks will do.

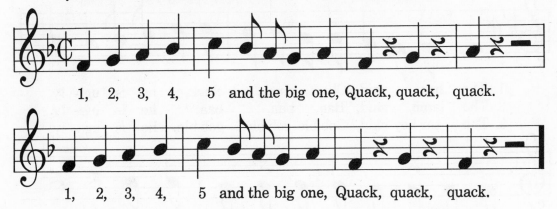

1,   2,   3,   4,   5   and the big one, Quack, quack,   quack.

1,   2,   3,   4,   5   and the big one, Quack, quack,   quack.

Soon five fuzzy little yellow ducklings came out of five eggs, and then,
out of the big egg came a big, funny-looking fellow. Mother Duck took
her six babies out on the pond for a swim, and as they swam she counted
them, as Mother Ducks will do.

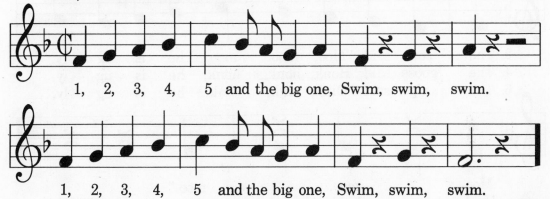

1,   2,   3,   4,   5   and the big one, Swim, swim,   swim.

1,   2,   3,   4,   5   and the big one, Swim, swim,   swim.

And everyone laughed at the big, funny-looking one.

1. The hen said, "Cluck, cluck, cluck, he is ug-ly,
3. The lamb said, "Baa, baa, baa, he is ug-ly,
5. The tur-key said, "Gob-ble, gob-ble, gob-ble, he is ug-ly,

Cluck, cluck, cluck."
Baa, baa, baa."
Gob-ble, gob-ble, gob-ble, gob-ble, gob-ble."

2. The cow said, "Moo, moo, moo, he is ug-ly,
4. The goose said, "Honk, honk, honk, he is ug-ly,
6. The pig said, "Oink, oink, oink, he is ug-ly,

Moo, moo, moo."
Honk, honk, honk."
Oink, oink, oink, oink, oink."

Well, the Ugly Duckling was so unhappy he ran away through the forest 'til he came to a little pond in the woods and there he saw four big white swans. The swans flew high in the air until they sailed away out of sight. He said, "Oh, I wish I were a white swan instead of an ugly duckling."

Soon fall came. The red leaves fell from the trees. The cold wind blew and the frost came and the ducks and geese were flying south for the winter; but the Ugly Duckling had no friends to show him the way, so he stayed. One day he was walking around the pond when he came to a little old house. A little old lady came out and said,

"Come in, come in! Come sit by the fire and spin.

You can live with me and my nice old cat,

And my lit-tle red hen so nice and fat.

Come in, come in! Come sit by the fire and spin,

And spin, and spin, and spin."

The Ugly Duckling said, "Thank you, dear little old lady!" and he went in the little old house.

The little old cat and the little old hen didn't like the Ugly Duckling.

1. Said the old cat, "Can you purr, catch mice, or meow?"
2. Said the old hen, "Can you cluck, lay eggs, or scratch?"

The duck-ling said, "Oh no, no, no, I can't do an-y-thing but swim!"
The duck-ling said, "Oh no, no, no, I can't do an-y-thing but swim!"

"But I can swim well."

"I swim round and a - round and a - round and a - round,

Round and a - round and a - round and a - round.

I swim round and a - round and a - round and a - round,

Round and a - round and a - round."

186

The cat said, "And get your fur wet?"
The hen said, "And get your feathers wet? We think you're silly."
The Ugly Duckling went back to his pond. It was getting very cold now, so to keep warm

He swam round and a - round and a - round and a - round,

Round and a - round and a - round and a - round.

He swam round and a - round and a - round and a - round,

Round and a - round and a - round.

But soon the pond was frozen over and the Ugly Duckling's feet were held fast in the ice. A farmer came along and took the Ugly Duckling home. The farmer's wife put him by the stove to get warm. When the farmer's children came home from school the poor duckling was so frightened he started to run around and round the kitchen with the happy children right behind him.

1. Run, lit-tle duck-ling, quack, quack, quack. Run, lit-tle duck-ling, quack, quack, quack.
2. Run, lit-tle chil-dren, run, run, run. Run, lit-tle chil-dren, run, run, run.

Run, lit - tle duck-ling, quack, quack, quack. Round and a - round and a-
Run, lit - tle chil-dren, run, run, run. Round and a - round and a-

round and a - round, And a quack, and a quack, and a
round and a - round, And a - round and a - round and a-

quack, And a quack and a - round and a - round and a - round.
round, And a - round and a - round and a - round and a - round.

Then out the door he ran 'til he came to a little pile of straw. He made a nest in the straw to keep warm and he ate the little grains of wheat the reapers had missed. All winter long he thought about the big white swans.

Then one day the Ugly Duckling looked out and he saw the leaves on the trees, flowers in the grass, and birds in the trees. He hurried down to the little pond in the wood. He was so happy it was spring.

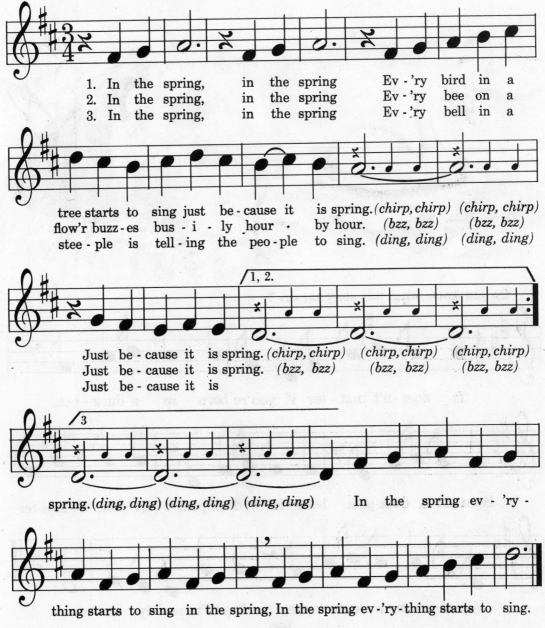

1. In the spring, in the spring Ev-'ry bird in a
2. In the spring, in the spring Ev-'ry bee on a
3. In the spring, in the spring Ev-'ry bell in a

tree starts to sing just be-cause it is spring. *(chirp, chirp) (chirp, chirp)*
flow'r buzz-es bus-i-ly hour by hour. *(bzz, bzz) (bzz, bzz)*
stee-ple is tell-ing the peo-ple to sing. *(ding, ding) (ding, ding)*

1, 2.
Just be-cause it is spring. *(chirp, chirp) (chirp, chirp) (chirp, chirp)*
Just be-cause it is spring. *(bzz, bzz) (bzz, bzz) (bzz, bzz)*
Just be-cause it is

3
spring. *(ding, ding) (ding, ding) (ding, ding)* In the spring ev-'ry-

thing starts to sing in the spring, In the spring ev-'ry-thing starts to sing.

Just then the Ugly Duckling saw the white swans floating on the little pond. The white swans came toward him and the Ugly Duckling was so ashamed of being ugly that he hung his head. But when he looked down in the water he could see himself just like in a mirror. And what do you think! He wasn't an ugly duckling at all. He was a swan! And when the children on the bank saw him they said, "Oh, look! He's the finest swan of all!"

Do you know what this story means?

It does-n't mat-ter if you're born in a duck-pen,

Born in a duck-pen, born in a duck-pen, It does-n't mat-ter

if you're born in a duck-pen, If you're real-ly a swan.

ALPHABETICAL INDEX

PRINTED IN THE UNITED STATES OF AMERICA